In a Marmalade Saloon

Patrick O'Connor wrote his first stories while still at school. The
years he spent in the Merchant Navy helped to form a literary
apprenticeship which also included experience in the Irish
'fit-ups' and London's little theatres. His short stories and plays
for the stage and radio have been produced and published in the
U.S. and Australia as well as Britain. A first novel, *Down the
Bath Rocks*, appeared in 1971.

Patrick O'Connor

In a marmalade saloon

Pan Books London and Sydney

First published 1974 by Hutchinson & Co (Publishers) Ltd
This edition published 1976 by Pan Books Ltd
Cavaye Place, London SW10 9PG
© Patrick O'Connor 1974
9 8 7 6 5 4 3 2
ISBN 0 330 24634 8
Printed and bound in Great Britain by
Richard Clay Ltd, Bungay, Suffolk

A bunch of the boys were whooping it up
in the Malamute Saloon . . .

Robert Service *The Shooting of Dan McGrew*

Contents

Part 1 The den

1

The time I like best in the den is when it's first thing in the morning and the doors have just been opened and the floors washed and the spittoons cleaned and fresh sawdust put in them. All the cues are in their racks, not lying about, and if you were to play a game you could pick the best cue. The marking boards are polished and the pin scoring boards wiped clean and there's a new piece of chalk ready for the first pin school.

Tammy Munn was ironing the tables and he said hullo Paddy. That's what they call me around the den. That and sometimes just Connor and sometimes Aconnor and even Pat. I've heard Patsy once but that's coming it a bit. It's mostly Paddy anyway in there. The only one who ever calls me Patrick is m'mother.

I said hullo Tam. His father, Jimmy Munn, owns the hall and they take it in turns to run it. We get on well because he practises his guitar in there when it's quiet and I know the jazz and the swing well and sometimes I help him out with a tune or even harmonize a bit until I get a red face and begin to feel all wasted. I get a red face very easy I don't know why.

He was running the big iron along the table just against the cushion over the nap and every table looked like a green that's just been mowed, smooth without a mark on them and not a ball been hit on them yet. It's a great feeling when you take a set of balls on to a table like that. When you put up, say, a set of snooker and triangle the red balls on the spot. And then just stand back and take a look, the pyramid of red balls glistening under the lights, all the colours lined up, yellow, green, brown, blue, pink and black. It's a sight for sore eyes, especially if it happens to be a set of new balls. I don't know a picture to beat it. It seems a pity to break the balls when it's like that.

I could see that Tam was a bit too busy to start gassing yet so I stood at the door and had a look at the corner.

It was only about half-past-nine and not many there. Only wee Red Joe Fitzpatrick who was always spinning yarns about the days of sail, with his Anchor Line sailor's jersey and that wee clay pipe or what was left of it, you'd think he'd buy himself another one and them only a penny as m'mother was always saying. Dublin Dan was leaning against the Royal Bank railings, spitting away like a toosher and telling the tale to Shorty Ramsay and Bagwash McBain.

There was one Midland motor standing at its stopping place. They're nearly always Leyland Lions or Tilling-Stevens but I've seen an old Jowett. They run to Glasgow but I've never seen anybody in them when they drive away except the driver and the conductress and they're nearly always city folk. Everybody I know gets the train. I used to get a penny for running for a jug of tea and buns to the Home Dairy for the conductress but I'm too big for that now, leave that for the wee boys. Two big polismen were standing at the Town Cross but they didn't look at me. I went back inside.

Tam had finished ironing the tables and he got his guitar out. He was wearing a great pair of navy blue flannel trousers with a belt of the same material that you would have to go to one of the good shops to get like Allisons in Prince's Street. And a light blue terry-towel sports shirt with lacing up the front like a football, the latest thing. He likes to put on the style. He can afford it if his father owns a billiards hall. He is a lot older than me, I don't know what age but he runs about

with a crowd of big bugs who wear college scarves nearly tripping them and have to slink in the back door of the Eglinton
Hotel if they want a drink, you'd think it was a crime.

– Who do you think will be King of Swing for nineteen thirty-
seven, Tommy Dorsey?

'I've always been a Benny Goodman man myself, so I said

– No. Benny Goodman.

– Aw ... That trombone in *I'm Getting Sentimental.*

– That clarinet in *Sing, Sing, Sing.*

– What about Artie Shaw's clarinet, is he not as good?

I get the feeling he pays attention to what I say about jazz. I
can see he thinks I'm a deep one. A lot of people say I am a
deep one. I'm not very sure if they all mean the same thing.

– Artie Shaw's not as good as Benny. He's more commercial
like.

– What about *Begin the Beguine*?

– Great. But Benny's the real jazz man, y'know?

I was in the den because it was no good looking for work on
Saturdays. Nobody was ever taken on for work on Saturdays
and even the ones who were lucky enough to have a job, the
Shell-Mex men, the Belfast boat men, the dockers at the iron
ore, anybody at all, only worked till twelve. The shipyard horn
blew at twelve o'clock and within five minutes you would see
them come rushing out the gates, some running to get changed
for the football, the boozers tripping themselves to get to
Nicol's Bar and the steady men hurrying home to their wives.

I didn't have a job yet even though I was turned sixteen,
because things were terrible bad everybody was saying. I was
only on the dole and going to the Unemployed School so I had
got up early, washed my face and took myself away out
although my mother nabbed me just before I got through the
door and told me to come back early and get a few things for
her because Bridget was coming down for the night from
Glasgow where she works as a maid in a big house.

Tam plugged his guitar in to convert it to electric Hawaiian
style and began to play *The Pagan Love Song.* He was only
halfway through the tune when Jack Carney came in and said
he would score a hundred and twenty to my hundred at billi-

11

ards. I don't know what he was doing in the hall at this time as he lives away up Glasgow Street. He is a right up-the-street one. A bit of a scunner as well. I said no he was too good for me. He offered me fifteen at snooker. I said no because I know he's hot and he talks you off your game as well. I've seen him playing for the team sometimes forbye – when they're stuck for a sixth cue.

But he was fairly trying to get me on and I wasn't having any then Spunky MacPartland came in and said

– Come on, leave the wee boy alone, I'll have you level at snooker.

Wee boy. And me past sixteen. I said to Spunky,

– Away, I'll be bigger than you, the now.

– Aye, that's right son.

He only laughed because he knows me well and used to live down our street before he became a bookie for himself. Anyway, I know I'm wee for my age. It makes me fed up and that's why I get a red face easy, especially when the lassies will not believe I've left school. I'm still in my first pair of long trousers. Grey flannels from Eddie Airds – twenty round the bottom and very gallus – that's as smart as you'll get, you know?

Tam put down his guitar and went to set the balls up for the game then Charlie Hands came in and said he would have me six or two. That's if you win you pay twopence and sixpence if you lose – eightpence a half-hour for the table. Charlie is one of my pals and he goes to the Unemployed School as well. We play level because we are a good match, sometimes I win one and sometimes he wins one. We went on for a half-hour at billiards, six or two.

A few came in after that and Tam had to put away his guitar in the office. It was getting quite crowded before we finished the game. Winkie Templeton had come in and he was getting up a school for five-pin pool for he is pin daft, every time he comes in everybody in the hall shouts *pins*. Carney said he would come in when he finished his game.

Charlie had a twenty-three break and beat me by twelve so that was a tanner dead. He wanted to go again but I said I'd

12

have to away and I would see him later. I didn't say anything
about going messages for m'mother because that's a bit soft,
you have to keep a bit quiet about things like that when you
go into long trousers.

2

It turned out m'mother wanted sausage links from the butchers
and a bag of wooden blocks for the fire from the sawmills to
save the coal a bit and I was to pay the week's papers at
Starks.

When I got back with this lot m'mother was preparing the
dinner and Annie was stuck, as usual, up the chimley with a
woman's magazine. M'mother began to tt-tt-tt.
– Come on you, Annie, you'll have to help me here to set the
table for your father is coming in and don't forget Bridget is
coming down from Glasgow to see us for the night.
– Oh, mammy, can I not finish this bit about William Corder.
I'm just at the bit where he gets hanged.
– No, come on you, this minute.
– Oh, all right.

She put the magazine under a cushion on the big chair,
looking at me as if to say don't touch it – as if I would read
one of them daft women's books – and began to get the things
out of the big press and lay them on the table. She left school
long before I did and she had a job once serving in Woolworths
and now she is a waitress in the Railway Hotel but only on
short time. She asked
– Is she coming on the train?
– She is of course, what do you think she would be getting, an
airyplane?
– Well, she could get the Midland motor.

As if anybody would be daft enough to get the Midland motor.

– Is she getting the night off from work?

– Yis.

– Has she got her own room there?

– Yes, she has. Come on now.

– Mammy, can I do that, tae? Can I be a maid and work in a swanky house like Bridget?

– Don't say *tae*. I'm forever telling you not to say *tae*. You would think you didn't know how to speak rightly. It's not *tae*. That's what the McGraws say next door and over Killmequick Street. Can you not say *as well*?

– Aye, but mammy—

– Ah, come on, you'll have me near distracted and you going on all the time like a canary. Patrick, son, did you get the links?

– Yes.

– Did you go to Guthries like I told you to and not to that old Argentines.

– Yes, and I got the *Rover* and the *Noon Record* for m'daddy's horses forbye.

– You'll never find me getting that old frozen meat from the Argentine butchers but the good steak links from Guthries. Did he put a wee bit of dripping in? He sometimes does if he knows you. Did you tell him it was for your mammy?

– He flung in a wee bit o' suet.

She still talks with a Belfast accent like the oldfella because that's where they both came from during what they call *the troubles* and sometimes *the royitts*. But Annie and I were born over this side and we speak like the rest of the people in the street but m'mother is always checking us for saying *pote* for pot or *heid* for head.

– Yis, that's right then. You should always go to the wee man with the moustache and not the other one.

– It was the woman that served me. And she laughed at me and made him fling in a wee bit o' suet.

Annie looked up from the table and said

– Have ye got the *Rover*?

14

– Aye, guess what Targa's doing this—
– I think that's a rotten book.
– What do—
– All they boy's books are daft. Not like the *Red Letter*.
– Listen to her.
– Come on you, Annie. Did you get that oul' *Record*, Patrick?
– Yes, m'daddy told me to get it last night.
– He's backing them horses and I don't know where he's getting the money from. You might as well put your money down the cesspool.

Then there was a commotion from across the landing in the McGraws' attic. Only an enclosed wooden stairs separate us and if you are up by our coalhouse door which is just inside the other door leading out to the stairs, you can hear everything that's going on. Sometimes m'mother goes over and puts her ear against the door and tells us all to be quiet till she can hear what's being said if she's at variance with Missus McGraw which is nearly always. It's like listening to the enemy's plans. At the bottom of the wooden stairs there are open stone stairs that take you to the close which leads out into the street or turn left at the bottom into the backyard. There is nothing much there except two lavatories shared between six families, a wash-house and the rubbish buckets at the top which are used as stepping stones by the Herald Street Gang taking a short cut over to their territory. That means the buckets are nearly always being knocked over on their sides with all the rubbish strewn all over the backyard and everybody shouting from their windows. But it doesn't do any good.

The McGraws were going their dinger, yelling blue murder, swearing, screeching and smashing the delf against the walls.
– Would you listen to that? That's they McGraws up to their performance again. Is that not terrible to have to listen to that? Words that no human ear should hear. Tt-tt-tt! To have to listen to that!

Just then m'father came in. He was blowing on his hands but that's a habit that he's got whether it's cold or not. He had a wee bottle of beer sticking out of each jacket pocket and moleskin trousers tied under each knee with string to kid everybody

15

on he was looking for work, I suppose. He always brings in some beer on Saturdays and puts the bottles under the set-in bed to last him for the week.

– It's brave and cold today... Aye...

– Do you hear what your childher have to listen to?

– Do I not? Aye, it's terrible, so it is. Terrible. I'll just put these two wee dumps under the bed.

He hung up his jacket on a hook on the back of the door and put the bottles of beer that he calls dumps under the set-in bed. I told him I'd got him the *Noon Record*.

– Aye, son, just put it in my coat pocket. And look at wee Annie. Ginger, you're balmy.

He walked over and patted her on the head.

She's got auburn hair and sometimes gets called Ginger. She patted her hair back into place again and swivelled this way and that in front of the looking-glass hanging on the wall.

– Oh, watch my hair, daddy!

– Oh yes, I forgot you're a fillum star now. You're getting more like Laura La Plante every day.

– Oh, daddy!

He rolled up his sleeves and went over to wash his hands. I said to her,

– Laura La Plante in *Tatties*.

– Oh you! He thinks he's Ramon Novarro, so he does.

– Away you, your hair's all tatties, anyway.

– Och you, Ben Hur.

– Now, come on you's childher and stop whingeing at one another. Sit up for your dinner.

She looked sideways at m'father washing his hands.

– Your big gerl's coming down from Glasgow to see us. I had a letter this morning.

– Oh, is Biddy coming down?

– You're not to call her Biddy. Now, she won't like you calling her that. You be calling her Bridget.

– Bridget.

We were all sitting at our dinner, m'father with his paper on the table beside him. Annie and I had to say Grace Before Meals together.

– Grace before meals bless us oh Lord and these thy gifts which we are about to receive from thy bounty through Christ our Lord amen.

My mother and father kept their heads bowed and their eyes closed till we had finished but they didn't join in. I said

– Mammy, am I not getting too big to say that?

There was a terrible crash from next door and another burst of screeching.

– Would you hear that? Is that not desperate? And the grace only out of their mouths.

Dan stood up, still chewing.

– Do you want me to go out to them? Bejings if I go out to them.

– No. No.

– I'll give him Davy McGraw ... Aye, I don't care if he is a fightin' man. He thinks he's the great fightin' man, so he does ... If Dan goes out to them ... You know what I am when I start?

– No, no, you've got a bit of drink in you. Sit down and take your dinner.

– Bejings if I go out to them, the fun will start, so it will, you'll see some fun ... Old Dan wasn't in the Sarshfield Guards for nothing!

But he was sitting down, all the same.

– Never mind, take you your dinner.

I asked him what he was in the Sarshfield Guards, was it in the Great War? And my mother said

– No, he played the flute so he did.

– And wasn't I the leader for a while, too? Wearing the white gloves. Sarshfield Guards – turn out!

– Yes, but who were you fighting, daddy? I said. Then Annie piped in.

– They weren't fighting. It was a band.

– Fighting? Aye, fightin', aye there was fightin' all right. It was the Falls Road against the Shankill Road.

– Ah, don't be talkin' about them things now. It's best that them things be forgotten.

I said to him,

–Did you win?

–It hasn't come to a decision yet.

My big brother John came in and hung up his coat and said

–Hullo.

All Annie could say to him was that he was late.

–Hay, John, I've got the *Rover*.

–Hullo, Patrick.

–There's the great wee working man, even if it is only a few shillings.

Saying this, m'mother smiled at him and I asked him if he had been out on the motor.

–Yes, Jimmy Stewart lets me out on his motor and he's to give me a few shillings. Any links, mammy?

–Aye, of course. There's some links and the good potatoes and a wee bit of beef ham for you because you're a working man. I've put it in a piece of bread and you can have a wee bit of dinner here and take the piece with you.

My father sang

–*For he's only a working man.*

I asked John what he did on the motor.

–I go in and collect the people's money after the motor's started, then I go out and stand on the back step and hold on to the rails till we get to Saltcoats. I'm in a hurry to get my dinner and I have to away out again.

The oldfella put on a pair of Woolworths' glasses to study the form of the horses and m'mother began to clear the table. I said to John,

–Do you help to get it started?

–Aye.

–Can you turn the handle?

–Aye.

Annie butted in again with,

–You'll break your wrist.

I made a terrible face at her.

–No, he couldn't. John's got the strength of Sampson. Are you getting to the pictures the night, John?

–Yes, I'm going to the *La Scala* with Laurence McEvoy.

M'father looked over his glasses and said
– I suppose you'll be looking for a couple of oul' gerls.
And that made Maggie give another tt-tt-tt.
– Whisht you, Dan, and don't be puttin' bad ideas into his head.

I asked John what the picture was.
– Bing Crosby in *We're Not Dressing*.

M'mother made a disapproving face at this and Annie turned her eyes away and her face got red. I told him I was going to see Victor McLaglen in *The King of the Khyber Rifles*.
– I've seen it. It's good.
– Eat up your dinner, son, or you'll be late.

Annie and I were still sitting at the table talking to John. I looked at her and she looked at me and we both began at the same time,
– We give thee thanks almighty God for all thy benefits, who livest and reignest, world without end, amen.

And Annie went straight on and said to John without stopping,
– The motor will go away without you.

I sneered at her again,
– No, it won't.
– Patrick, would you go in under the bed and get me out that form book that's in behind the washing bine. Don't get lost in there among the oul' cockroaches.

As I went in to do this, Annie was saying
– Eugh! Gads! Oh, daddy, don't talk about them things. Oh, it makes me all shivery.

And as I came out, my mother was saying
– No, those are dirty things, so they are. I could never thole those things.
– They'd go up your legs.

John jumped up from the table saying he would have to away, putting on his cap and pulling the peak well down over one eye. M'father said to him,
– If you hook that skip down any more, you'll only be able to see out of one eye.

Annie said the other fellas were calling him the Hooker-Down and John turned on her,

– It's the right way to wear your bunnet, so it is. It's the style. Spunky MacPartland the bookie wears his that way. It's all the fashion in Glasgow. You's don't know, so you's don't. I'm away.

– Here's your piece, son.

M'mother gave him some sandwiches wrapped in newspaper as he went out the door. She shouted after him,

– Don't be late for your tea, son! ... I'm away down to the spicket to gut these herrings for the tea. Mind you, Annie, and watch that kettle on the hob.

– Yes. All right.

She went away out carrying a plateful of herrings to be gutted. There's only one spicket with fresh running water for the whole of the tenement and that is down in the backyard. If anybody else is using it you have to wait your turn. Water for drinking and washing has to be carried up in a pail. We've got a white enamel one. As soon as she was out the door, the oldfella said

– Here, Patrick, I want you to take a wee line round to Mick Kelly.

He got a piece of paper from the dresser and a stub of pencil and began to write.

– Here. A wee tanner double. *Precipitation* in the three-thirty at Ayr and *Easter Hero* in the three o'clock at Aintree. If cash, a shilling win on *Eric's Pal*. Don't let on to your mammy where you're going.

– She'll not see me if I jump over the wall into McNamee's backyard.

– That's right. And I'll see you all right if I have a win. Don't you be saying anything, Annie hen.

– Oh, I don't know anything about it. I have to go out with m'mammy to help her carry the messages and then I'm coming back to put on my good dress and go to the dance at the Castlecraigs with Margaret Morgan.

I made a face like Eddie Cantor at her and said whoopee and made her giggle and ran away out like a hare.

3

Harbour Place was quiet when I went out into it. I suppose most of them were still at their dinner or the men having a sleep on the big chair after. The sun was shining over the Church of the Nazarene throwing the usual pattern of palings on the granite chips at the Bute Place corner. When I got into Prince's Street a Clyde Coast motor drew up at the Lyric picture house – which used to be called the Princes – out jumped John McAllister and he ran like hell for the station, all red in the face with his tie loosened. He works as an engineer in the shipyard but he also plays for Albion Rovers, a Coatbridge team. And when he finishes at twelve on Saturday he has a mad rush to catch the train from Ardrossan to Glasgow and then to wherever they're playing. He went through school about five years ahead of me and then he went on to Saint Micks, the college. I shouted come away the Albion to him but he hardly had the wind to answer me. Before I went through the station gates I heard a carriage door banging and the train puffing away out of the station so he must have just made it. The gates were open as I got there and I didn't have to cross the bridge. Up on the billboards it said The Lovely Firth of Clyde and there was a picture of the *S.S. Glen Sannox* and Sailings from Ardrossan by the Steam Packet, *Atlanta*.

Round the signal box into the Inches Road and along by the low railway dyke. Across the lines you can see McKinnon's back windows. Missus McKinnon was cleaning one of the windows and she looked across but I don't think she saw me.

Not very far to the huts beside the muck dump. The sun was shining behind them and the glare reflecting from the sea. The *S.S. Atlanta* was coming in from Troon, just passing Battery Point at the end of Inches Road. After tying up at Winton Pier and picking up passengers it would head for Arran – Brodick and Lamlash. I made my way towards the huts. The flute band hut. The bookie's hut. The hut in which Jimmy Stewart keeps his motor. A crowd of men standing around studying the

21

papers and trying to pick winners and two of them watching for the polis.

I have to march through this lot and up to Mick Kelly himself standing just inside the door of the hut at a kind of desk they've made with a telephone on it. This is the bit I hate. All the men look at you and wink at each other and say something they think is funny and I scringe my teeth and try and look like Benny Lynch or somebody that would frighten them off. Mick Kelly opens the line slowly and takes the tanner out as if it was a nugget of gold while I stand there with a red face, he reads it and says that's a bet and all the big guys around kill themselves laughing. I usually just kind of snarl at them but I have to walk away again with their eyes boring into my back.

But it wasn't so bad this time being Saturday and very busy. Nobody took much notice of me and I slunk through the crowd and out again like a whippet.

4

There was only m'father and me in that afternoon sitting by the fire and he had his pipe going and was telling me the tale as usual.

– Yes, ye see it was the medical students, that's who it was y'see. That's who it was was doing it all. The people were disappearing right, left and centre all over Belfast. The gerls were affeared of their life to go out when it was dark. Didn't your Aunt Maggie have a near escape herself. Yes, it was only a bit of luck, so it was. . . .

He took a real good spit in the fire here. And about time, too, his pipe was beginning to sound a bit bronchial. The spit sizzled on the hot bars and slid down in bubbles and blobs and ended up with the other stalactites or is it stalagmites hanging on the grate. But he would always knock them off with the poker when there were too many. And he never left any when he finished his smoke. I've never seen more than three stalactites hanging at one time.

– And your Aunt Maggie was a quare an' good-lookin' gerl, you know. And she was a great dancer, oh, a great dancer and play the melodeon as well. Yes, this big cab drew up. Yes, right in the middle of Royal Avenue ... Out steps this fella. A big toff, you know. He says to her take this note to such and such a place ... my little gerl. He gave her half-a-sovereign ... Run all the way, he says.

Spit. Sizzle. Stalactite. Two in the game, striker up.

– Him dressed up with a top hat, too ... And away she goes. But, as luck would have it ... didn't she fall down after tripping over something in her hurry. And the note opened out. Aye, an'd'ye know what was in the note? Aye, d'ye'know?

– No.

– *Hold the bear till I go there*
And I will be her butcher. Yes.
Hold the bear till I go there
And I will be her butcher. Yes. They were cutting up the bodies. They couldn't get enough dead bodies so they couldn't and they were starting on anyone they could get their hands on. Yes, them medical students it was. They're terrible bad so they are, you know, them medical students.

Spit. Sizzle. Three up. Game to Dan.

– Yes, the fear of your life in Belfast...

A newspaper boy in the street calling *Times, News, Citizen,* racing and football results.

– Here, there's the paper. Run out and get the paper, Patrick, and I'll get the results. Away, quick and catch him.

The boy was shouting at the bottom of the stairs and I jumped out quick and nabbed him and brought the *Evening Citizen* back in to the oldfella. He grabbed it from me with one hand, putting on his glasses with the other.

– Now, wait to we see. Let me see, now. The three-thirty. Aye. Van ... Who was this was up on that? Yis. That's not a bad price. No, he came with the other one. And that one at Ayr.

Yes ... Aha! Yes, that's right. Bejings, your oul' daddy has a wee double up, yes. A wee double. It's not much, mind you ... I'll give you something to yourself. Don't you be letting on.

He put his glasses in his waistcoat pocket and went for his jacket.

– I might be able to catch Mick Kelly at the corner.

– Are you going out, daddy?

– Yes, I'll see if I can catch him at the corner.

– What will I tell m'mammy?

– Tell her I've went out to get a breath of air about me.

He hurried away out. I went over to the window. There was a *True Romances* magazine sticking out from behind a cushion on the big chair. I listened to hear if there was anybody coming up the stairs. Sometimes you see advertisements for women's corsets or knickers with a picture. I took it over behind the big iron bed near the door so that I could hear a foot on the stairs. Some of the stories had photos and I found one with a woman lying back on a sofa with her skirts creased up so that you could see her legs right up over her knees. I was wondering if I held it slantwise would I be able to see up further maybe up past her garters, knowing that I wouldn't be able to but still trying when I heard m'mother's and Annie's voices approaching. I just had time to stuff the book back under the cushion again and stand at the window so they wouldn't see the bulge in my trousers before the door opened.

– ... *another sunny honeymoon.*

Another season, another reason

For making whoopee.

– Glasgow Street is crowded again ... Put that down there. Patrick, come and help me, here.

– Wait a minute. *Picture a little love nest ...*

– What d'ye mean, wait a minute?

Her voice was suspicious. But that is not unusual.

– What are you singing songs out the window for, do you want the McGraws to think you're daft?

– Eh. Wait a minute.

– Come over you here, this minute or I'll turn another pin in your nose.

She has got a lot of these old sayings that sound very impressive but you would rack your brains trying to think out what they mean. Anyway, it was safe so I went over.
– Where's your father?
– He went out.
– Where did he go to?
– He went out for a breath of air.
– A breath of air? A breath of something else.
  Annie said
– Will I put the potatoes in the old basin, mammy?
– Yes, a breath of something else ... The same old sixpence.
– Mammy?
– Yes, put them in the old tin basin. We'll have to hurry up as Bridget will be here soon. Come on, Annie, and we'll get the table laid.

5

As it was Saturday night there was no question of staying in. After my tea I waited at the Lyric Picture House corner for Charlie Hands where he would catch the bus into Saltcoats. Bridget hadn't arrived yet and John would be still out on his motor as it was a busy night. Leaky Williamson came out of the Lyric looking miserable as usual.
– Is the picture any good in the Lyric?
– No. Don't go. It's rotten. It's an English picture.
  As if I would. A look at the photos outside is enough. Binkie K. Barnes or somebody in Who Shot The Peasants Up Badgers Close. Or Back The Cairt Up the Hoarses Arse as Jimmy Geary, the Co-operative milkman would say. We never went to see an English picture if we could help it for they were always about badgers or birds' nests or dogs or people who

looked like badgers or birds' nests or dogs floundering about in the muck with the rain soaking them, always with one hand up to their eyes, scanning the horizon for something they've lost. And you could bet your parish boots it would be a dog if it wasn't a sailing ship being tossed in the waves off the coast that you could see a mile away was only a tanner boat out of Woolworths in a basin.

– Did Winton Rovers win?

I told him they beat Kilbirnie Ladeside four, two and he went away up Hill Street. I was glad he wasn't trying to come with us as I've sat beside him in the pictures before and he picked his nose all through the big film, it would give you a right scunder to your dinner.

I looked round the corner and Charlie was just rolling past Agostini's ice-cream shop. He is very broad built and walks like a sailor although he has never been to sea but he has had the notion a couple of times. He is as sound as a bell and would never see you stuck for the price of the pictures or sub you half a dollar to keep you in the pin school.

I went round to meet him and we stood at the stop waiting for the bus. He gave me a Woodbine and we lit up. Up at the corner it was getting busy, boozing crowds forming and pals meeting, those with jobs very sharp with gallus London Tan double-breasted suits with padded shoulders and those on the dole, that is the majority, with only a muffler and a cap but Rab Walker, the biggest proguer of Harbour Place showing himself up with the arse out of his trousers. Wee Red Joe was still there, his pipe shorter than ever, I'm forever blowing bubbles, he should bring his bed with him to the corner. The usual two polismen in their capes keeping their eye on everything, exercising their knees and waiting for shutting-time when they could run in the drunk men.

Granny Macmillan who scrubs out the pubs and likes a drop of the biddy they say, was having one at the polis, she would have a few in her by this time. Now and again she would put her fist under their noses and shake it but they were not taking any notice of her and they had to laugh. She broke off now and again to sing a chorus or two of *The Bonny Lass of Balloch-*

myle and ended up by doing the Highland Fling. She was still wearing her old sugar-bag working apron and men's tackety boots with thick grey woollen socks rolled down over her own stockings. As she danced she lifted up her skirts with a *hooch*! and her black stockings and grey elastic garters began to work slowly down her legs and when she got out of breath and had to stop, the whole corner gave her a cheer. She's a great turn.

Jay Regan, the greatest boozer in the West was there also, going around from group to group trying to raise the price of a drink. They say he'll drink Brasso if he can get nothing else. I've even heard he would melt down boot polish but that takes a bit of believing. He would do an odd job from time to time. That is, when he hasn't got the horrors or been put in Barlinnie gaol. Monkey Nuttall, as full as a lord, came into view, making his way from paling to paling around the Royal Bank of Scotland corner and he was getting a good crowd. The trouble is he ran out of palings very early and thought he would travel the rest of the way by paving stone. The idea being to hang on the edge of the kerb and pull himself hand over hand, supported by a foot on the wall now and again whenever it touched. When the polis began to get interested in him, two of the fellas went over, picked him up and, supporting him between them, linked him in the direction of Herald Street and home.

Outside the Ship Bar, Wullie McGraw who goes to sea as a fireman when he can get a ship was telling everybody within hearing what he would do to Bean Mann if he caught him with Bessie Wilson again. They have a permanent barney on and whenever one gets enough drink he goes gunning for the other one. Practically any Saturday night if you go up Hill Street, just up the Cannon Hill steps behind the big rock beside the Drill Hall, you'll see them knocking lumps out of one another while Bessie Wilson coories up a close halfway down the street waiting for the winner.

Anyway, the Kilmarnock bus of the A.1. Service came round Glasgow Street corner and me and Charlie got on, nipping our fags because there's no smoking. We had plans for getting hold of a couple of wee sneckers if we could. We

followed two up and down Dockhead Street but lost them before we could make our intentions known. We tried the
Ca'dora fish and chip shop where a few of the boys and girls
gather but all the Saltcoats boys of the Quay Street gang were
there scooting the vinegar bottles at each other and creating
pandemonium and they would have murdered us. It was time
to get into the queue for the *Countess* forbye which was right
down to the Woollen Hosiery. There was no talent in our bit of
the queue either but we got in all right and the big picture was
good, Victor MacLaglen shot about a hundred natives.

6

When I got home that night quite late my mother had her up-
the-chimley vale of tears face on. She was sitting beside the fire
with Bridget and Annie one on each side of her like the
daughters of Jerusalem. Something up. The air was so heavy
that Bridget only just managed to acknowledge my existence
and I couldn't even ask her what she had brought me from
Glasgow.
  – The boyo's not coming in, you know. I know. I know your
father. That's him away. Yes. The same old sixpence ... Yes.
You would think that for once with his eldest daughter coming
home, he would be here. Oh no, but not Dan, oh no, not Dan
... I suppose ... Some company ... He's got into some
company. He's had a winner, that's what it is. Did he have a
winner, Patrick, did he have a winner? You wouldn't say ...
You can tell your mother, go on sure there's no harm to you.
Did he have win, eh? Did he have a win?
  – I don't know. Maybe he did.
  – He would have told you, so he would. Did he send you
round to get his winnings?
    I had to play safe here but Annie sounded as if she was

ready to spill the beans at any minute, as she said

– He always sends you round, so he does.

– You shut up. No, he didn't send me. He said he was away
out to get a breath of air about him.

– A breath of air, aye, a breath of the oul' drink is more like it.
An' I know the breath of air. As soon as I heard the breath of
air business, I knew what was up, so I did.

All Bridget could say from the heights of Jordanhill,
Glasgow was,

– Never mind, mother, don't get yourself into a state, maybe
he will be home soon.

She speaks a bit pan loaf because she used to serve the
quality in my auntie's high-class confectioners in Derry before
auntie became bankrupt and lost everything.

– Terrible. And your coming down from Glasgow to see us and
all ... You'll sleep in the big bed with Annie and me ... And
bringing us all down wee presents as well and here *he* is, standing I suppose in some old bar or other bumming his chat and
making an oul' cod of himself more than like.

– I heard him sending Patrick with a line.

I knew she would give the show away. I said

– Ah, you're an old tell-tale, so you are, wait till I tell m'daddy
on you.

– Oho, you went with a line did you? If you had been a bit
younger, I would have given you a good skelp on the lug.

– Well, I only went with the line because he told me to but I
never went round with any winnings.

Bridget made her mouth like a prune and looked at me like
a schoolteacher in the Advanced Division sitting on the Dux
Medal. M'mother began her spiel again.

– Aye, an' I'll warrant you it's come up an' he's away. Oh, I
know him too well. There are things I could tell ye's ...

And no doubt she would.

– If ye's only knew. Aye, Bridget here could tell you. Oh yis.
Bridget knows what I had to suffer. Oh, the Lord only knows
... Aye ... It's not the first time he threw his wages into the
fire, so it isn't. Yes, threw all his wages into the fire, every
penny, and him mad with drink. And I had all the weans to

feed. And not a copper piece to put in their mouths. Yes ...
Only Bridget here helped me to rake the half-crowns out of the
red cinders, so she did, and a few coppers.

Bridget sat looking like Blessed Margaret Sinclair.

– And all the rest went up the chimley. Yes. Threw his pay
into the fire. John was fair and big, Annie was only young and
Patrick wasn't born. Isn't that right, Bridget?

– Yes, it is that. And many a time I had to go out looking for
him to get some money off him to keep us before he went into
the pub.

– Yes, that's right. Yes, she can tell you. And he was even
worse before we left Belfast.

Suddenly there was the sound of a commotion coming from
the stairs and the street. Loud shouting and banging. Scuffles
and a bottle smashing.

– Oh, Jesus, Mary and Joseph, that's him. Oh, my God that'll
be him. I know it in my bones. He's got into trouble, so he
has.

The banging and shouting was even louder.

– Oh, dear God. Oh, if I go out it will make him worse.

Annie was biting her lips and screwing up her face then she
gave up.

– Oh mammy, I'm going to run away. Oh, what'll we do.

She began to cry. Bridget said

– I'll go down to him, mother.

– No, don't you go.

– He'll not hit me. He hasn't seen me for a while.

But Bridget wasn't allowed to go by my mother who now
turned to Annie,

– There. There now. It's all right. Sure, he won't touch you.
It's all right. The playboy is up to his old tricks again, so he is
... Out on the ran-dan ... His mother, God rest her, blamed
his brother, your Uncle John. Uncle John and one of his
cronies gave him a bottle and told him it was only lemonade
... and he never stopped from that day to this. Aye, the quare
lemonade it was.

More shouting. I was dying to get out into it.

– Mammy, will I go out and help?

30

– Yes, son, slip you out and see if it's him and try to get him home. He'll listen to you. He always listens to you.

– Right mammy, I'll jump over McNamee's wall and slip round the front.

I tore out of the house and down the stairs two at a time.

7

When I got on to the stone steps I could see a crowd in McNamee's backyard pushing that way and this and all shouting at the tops of their voices. I looked out over the top of them in the light of the gas lamp that hangs over the big entry which leads into the yard and they call the big pen. They seemed to be more or less divided into two separate lots milling backwards and forwards and sometimes mingling but somehow it was more like a market than a battlefield. In the centre of one crowd was Davy McGraw waving his arms about and shouting blue murder and the other lot was holding up the oldfella. I didn't wait to see any more but shinned over the dyke into the thick of it.

I half landed on top of Micky Boyle and two others who were sitting down under the wall sharing a screwtop beer bottle on the sidelines of the rammy and first of all he was going to massacre me and then when he saw who it was,

– Is that wee Patrick?

He was up on his feet and telling me never to fear, the Irish would not be defeated that night, no, never be beaten so they wouldn't.

I managed to winkle through the crowds surging about and over to the old man and began trying to attract his attention and pulling at his arm but he and the crowd around him were all shouting together and I couldn't make any impression at all, I don't think he even saw me. I then switched my plans to penetrating into the enemy camp as a spy to find out what the strength was. I got to the fringe of our side and, being careful to always keep a row of friends between myself and the outer guards of the enemy, I caught sight of Davy McGraw's family. Mustered were Wullie, Jimmy, young Joey, Geordie and Robert, that's from the eldest to the youngest, leaving out the girls. They were dancing around in a ring doing a war dance and singing

— *Tarry-um-a-dee,*
  The monkeys up a tree
  Ate all the coconuts
  And left nane for me!

Then they would stand still suddenly, raise their arms in the air and all shout together,

— *Umbree!*

Don't ask me what this meant. But there had been a jungle picture at the Lyric matinee not long since featuring Elstree cannibals and one look at the McGraws left me not needing to be convinced that they would eat me if they caught sight of me without thinking twice about it. So I put enough space between me and them to allow for safety. This brought me outside an old back window. The sill was free so I climbed up on it and stealthily spied the land. I was able to get a good view of Davy McGraw, the champion of the other side. The centre of a jostling, dragging group, he had his jacket half-on and half-off, throwing himself about and punching the air with his fists. He was drunk, but not as much as the old man, and a steady stream of language was being hurled at the skies.

— Let him fughinwell come o'er here the fenianbastar an' I'll fughinwell maul him do you see that fist that's fughinwell beat bigger and better men than that fughin tattie howker d'you know what they are them papishbastars comin' over here to eat us out o' house and hame from the fughin bogs a lot of aul' fughinbogtrotters tell me! tell me? I'll fughinwell melt him I'll kick the fughinshite outy him I'll smash his fughinlights in the cun I'll kick his fughinarse back to the fughin shough where he came from . . .

He convinced me. I didn't wait to hear any more but jumped

down and made my way through the crowd again, searching
for the oldfella. I could make out his voice but I couldn't see
him. Then I began to hear snatches in the accents of our side
and I knew I was getting near our camp.

– Aye, ye will ... He's asking for it, so he is ... Give him a
fughinthumpin, Dan ... He's only a fughinoul' murphydite so
he is. We fughinbate them before an' we'll fughinbate them
again. A lot of oul' jackals. They never paid man nor baste.
They're on the fughinprogue from morn till night. They'd lift
the eye out of your fughinhead. You're the boy, Dan. Sure, ye
bate better men nor him. D'ye see that? Give him that. Kick
the fughintripes outa him ...

The object of all these big fight preliminaries looked as if he
was far from the land away making his last stand on Tara's
hill. Although his fists were up and his jacket was off – showing the big hole in the back of his shirt – and there was a glint
of beery battle in his eye, it looked to me that, if the gang
pressing round him had moved away, he would fall flat on his
back. The crowd around him would pull him round so that he
was sometimes facing east and sometimes facing west, but
always with his fists up ready to charge in whatever direction
he was pointed.

A surge of the crowd brought Davy McGraw unexpectedly
heading this way, penetrating our ranks and creating panic
both amid his own following and the following of the oldfella.

Dan, held up by Micky Boyle on one side and Paddy
McNamee on the other, was turned round to face the threat.
Dan shouted

– Let him come! Let him come on! Sarshfield Guards, turn
out!

Davy McGraw shouted

– Where is he? Where is he?

The two camps swirled around slowly in opposite directions
and, just as the two champions got within five yards of each
other, the swirl took them further away again.

– Go on Davy, murder him! ... Come on, Dan, he's affeared
of you, so he is ... You've got the beatin' of him, Davy ...
You'll wear him down, Dan ... Kick his fughin melts in,

Davy ... Mind his left, Dan ... Come on, O'Connor! ... Up
the McGraws! ... Put the fughinboot in, Davy ... Take the
pins from him, Dan ... Watch out for his right, Davy! You're
outlasting him Dan, so you are ...

– I'll massacre him! Where is he, where is he?

– He'll never bate me, so he won't. Sarshfield Guards, turn
out!

– Umbree!

I found myself carried back to McNamee's window again
and climbed back on to the sill just in time to see John coming
in through the big pen. I shouted to him and he saw me and
came towards me, getting through the crowd easily because of
his strength. He shoved his jacket into my hands, asking me to
hold it, rolled up his sleeves and dived into the crowd again.

I looked out over the crowd and by this time the swirl was
bringing the champions around face to face again. This time
the crowd halted, eddied about and suddenly melted away in
one part leaving the champions facing each other with their
fists up. Even the man who had been holding the oldfella up
retired to the ringside leaving him standing alone. He looked
as if the movement of a finger or a breeze springing up would
be enough to unbalance him.

Davy McGraw, less drunk, began to circle around a bit,
move his fists up and down and make what was supposed to be
bloodcurdling battle cries but to me sounded like Tammy
MacNamara shouting ripe bananas. And whichever way he
weaved, the oldfella swivelled glazedly in that direction without moving his feet.

– Go on, McGraw! ... Go on Dan, you're doing fine ...
Give him the left, Davy! Uppercut him, Dan!

Suddenly, Davy McGraw seemed to swallow hard, take a
deep breath and launch himself at Dan, fists flailing. But, at
the same time, John appeared and fairly hurtled out of the
crowd, throwing himself in front of the oldfella with arms
outstretched. Paddy McNamee and Micky Boyle sprang out
from the sidelines and placed themselves one on each side of
the oldfella again, preventing him from falling over. Davy
McGraw's seconds closed in around him, patting him on the

34

shoulder and generally praising him. The ranks were closed
and the enemy retired behind his stockade again.

It was all over then. John's strength, not to be resisted, pro-
pelled Dan in a homewards direction, linked by his two faith-
ful lieutenants and pushed by me from the back, leaving the
auld enemy also making signs of packing up for the night –
both parties, of course, shouting to the world just what they
wouldn't do to the other one and that it was a good thing for
him ...

8

When we got home I ran up the stairs and got in first.
– M'daddy was in a fight!
– Oh, God save us, where is he? Who was he fighting with?
I'd better go to him.

Annie was crying harder than ever.
– It was Davy McGraw. But it's all right, mammy. John came
round the corner in the nick of time and got between them.
– Did he? Did he?
– Micky Boyle and Paddy McNamee are helping him home.
The whole street was turned out but the polis didn't come.
– Disgracing himself again. There y'are. A disgrace. He would
disgrace us all. And him saying he had settled down? He'll
never settle down till he's in his grave, God forgive me.

The oldfella was linked up the stairs and into the attic with a
great clatter. He managed to stand up by himself by holding on
to the back rail of the big bed so, thanked by Maggie, Micky
Boyle and old Paddy made themselves scarce. Dan's eyes were
focusing better and he was beginning to find his voice again.
– No ... I'm ... I'm a maan, so I am. D'ye know that? I'm a
maan. I was not. D'you see. I was ... I'll take them on. Oh, I'll
take them on ... so ... so I will. The Sarsh ... The Sarshfiel'

Guar's. Sarsh Guar's, turn out! He shouts to them, turn out! Turn out! Dan. Dan was leadin' the band then. Dan. Dan ... was leadin' the band. An' the other fellas lyin' in wait. Yis. Lyin' in ambush. It was an ambush, so it was. D'ye mind that, Maggie?

– Yes. Come and sit down on the chair then, by the fire.

– I'll sit down on no chair! You'll not get me into any chair! Don't you ... Don't you ... you try and get me into the chair. I'll stand ... I'll stand up on my hind legs, so I will.

He nearly overbalanced at this and John had to prop him up again.

– I'll stand up on my own two hind legs. As I ... The same ... The same as ... The day they were lying in ambush ... Yis ... They stoned the train. Stoned the train, so they did. Stoned ... Isn't that right? Smashed. All they smashed the windows. The women and the children. They had to lie down on the floor. Oul' Dan, so he ... Dan ... Portrush. Yes, Portrush it was. The day's outing to Portrush ... You'll never get me to sit down, so you won't ... The band's outing to Portrush ...

– That's right, they stoned the train, so they did. They were lying in wait for us. That's right. Come on then, Dan—

– I'm a maan! So I am. And wasn't Dan out? Was' Dan out? Burlin' the pike around his head. Yis, out the train ... Down the line, burlin' the pike around his head ...

– That's right. He rallied us all, so he did. I'll say that much for him, God help him.

– I'm a maan! I'll give him fightin', I'll give him Davy McGraw. Davy McGraw? Davy McGraw? I'll give him fightin'.

– Whisht Dan, he'll hear you and be comin' in to you.

– Ye know what I'm like when I start. Yis, ye know what I'm like ... Do you want me to start? You'll see some fun, so you will.

He made a mistake, let go of the bed rail and began to pitch forward. Grabbing desperately at the table, he knocked two plates off, smashing them and ended up flat out on the floor. He was floundering about, trying to get up again when John went over and held him down.

– Holy God, he'll tumble over the lamp and set the house on fire! That's right, you hold him, son. Ah, it's God's holy wisdom that gave you the strength so that you could hold him. I don't know what we'd all do if it wasn't for the boy here.

He had the strength of two men. Talk about Tarzan. He was looking up at us, showing off a bit. His muscles were like cannon balls.

– Aye. Aha ... Ye think you can beat your oul' father do ye? But I'm ...

He tried to break John's grip but he couldn't. That's not to say that he wouldn't have been able to when sober, fair's fair.

– I'm a maan ...

We all stood with our mouths open as John, after a bit of a struggle, picked up the oldfella bodily, staggered with him over to the set-in bed and dumped him inside. He loosened his tie and undressed him a bit and all we heard out of Dan after that was snoring.

– Ah, Lord save us, did you see that? There's the brave boyo to his mammy. His strength is coming out now. The good strength that God gave him to save us all!

9

Out in the morning on the way to half-past-eleven Mass – sez you! – but sleeking up the shortcut at South Beach putting green, over the iron bridge to the Castle Hill again, across and down Hill Street, creep along Hill Place and climb over Toner's wall to Montgomerie Street, slinking into the den about twenty-five to twelve when all the chapel-goers would be safely inside and had their first blessing forbye.

The smell of nice and early in the den again, cues neat-racked and tables with that mowed field look, the floors still damp-patched and smelling of cleaning fluid, the back door opened to let the air in and the sun beginning to shine through the big skylights so that you wouldn't need any table lights. Wouldn't it be great if it could stay like that all the time, you sometimes think. But by closing time the floor will be knee deep in fag-ends, the spittoons claghered up, the cues lying about and you won't be able to see to the other end of the hall for cigarette reek.

It was a very quiet morning. But after a while Joe Townsley came in so I could find out who said half-past-eleven Mass and what the sermon was about to kid on the old lady if she tried to catch me. He said it was Father Mooney and the sermon was about missing Mass on Sundays through your own fault and how it was one of the most terrible sins of all. I just hope I don't get hit with the back end of a cue today or brained with a billiard ball otherwise I'll be playing my last frame with Old Nick, striker down.

As there was nothing much doing in the den, Charlie and I went over the Bath Rocks to watch the big tossing schools. That was the day Tommy Morgan headed nineteen times without a tail-two and only twelve head-tails. The bets went from pennies into heavy metal and then notes before the end. He must have won a stack. I don't believe the tossing pennies were loaded. A lot say they must have been, you couldn't head them nineteen times. But I saw him doing it and Charlie is my witness. Nineteen times before tailing them. And the kind of school he was in, loaded pennies would get you a striped face, delightful swimming facilities at the end of the sewage pipe and a permanent holiday bungalow near the North Pole.

Nineteen times. You want to have seen the crowd around him. You could have dropped a pin and nobody would have heard it. Tommy, hypnotised, kind of caressing the pennies in mid-air, stroking them, invoking them, talking to them, twin butterflies fuseying in the air and always the magic heads appearing, not a breath, every eye on them, can he do it again? The chanting of the tosser's litany.

– *Up they go, sky blue,*
  Down they come – head-two!
  The big Hampden roar as he did it again.

And so he went down in the history books. And you can still see today the grotto on the Bath Rocks where he did it. He should get a statue.

After my dinner I went behind the curtains of the set-in bed and lay down to read a cowboy book that John had lent me. Besides me, there was only Bridget and the old lady in. They were sitting by the fire with their heads together having a good gabble, thinking I couldn't hear them, I suppose.

– Yes. Tom McGrath. Yes.

– They're all the same, you know. I tould you, Bridget. I warned you long ago, didn't I?

– Yes. You did right enough.

– My mother, God rest her, used to say *The mark of the beast*. Yes, the mark of the beast.

– Mark of the beast, all right.

– There's that bit in them, y'see.

– Yes. It was all right walking home. And going to the pictures. Then ... And then ... It was ... Of course it was his way he wanted. He wanted to have his way.

– Tt-tt-tt-tt-tt!

– We'll get engaged, he says.

– Oh, tt-tt-tt!

– But it wasn't the getting engaged. I got the shock of my life. I never thought he was like that, you know.

– Well, he was always dressed up like a fish supper.

– And his soft hat and his astrakhan gloves.

– But didn't he wear them pointed shoes, too.

– But he wasn't a bit gallus, mother. I think he thought he was the gentleman, y'know?

– Och, he was a bit stuck-up when all's said and done.

– Some gentleman ... I never thought ... I never thought for a minute he would ever go too far, y'know?

– Ah, they all want the one thing, daughter.

– Used to walk me home. Up the avenue, you know. Then we'd stop by the bushes.

– Aye, the bushes. Oh, they're great ones for the bushes. A-ha-ha! Yis, in among the bushes, as they said.

— I didn't mind ... You know ... I mean ... I didn't mind ...
A goodnight kiss. But ... Oh ...

— Aye, a goodnight kiss. Then one thing leads to another.

— Oh, but I made it quite clear. *I'm not a girl of that sort, at all*, I said.

— You were never brought up to that sort of thing.

— No. So I said *You're making a big mistake Mister Thomas McGrath. What do you think I am?* I nearly slapped his face, y'know?

— A good skelp in the face brings them to their senses.

— Stops their nonsense. Yes, I said. *You've got the wrong girl, Mister Thomas McGrath, even if you have got a double-breasted overcoat and all your orders.*

— That's the way to tell them.

— And here ... They'll never take no for an answer ... I said *You can't have any respect for me*, I said, *or you wouldn't behave like ... like an animal.*

— Oh! Did you say that?

— I didn't make any bones about it. You should've seen the way he looked at me.

— He was a Catholic too, wasn't he?

— A member of the Sacred Heart Confraternity.

— What!

— As sure as I'm sitting here.

— Oh, in the name o' God!

— Says I *You know you're defiling that badge you have in your breast.*

— Oh! Tt-tt-tt!

— He hung his head then.

— He knew.

— He was ashamed so he was, I'll say that much for him. I could see that. But ... My next night off ... He was as bad as ever again.

— What makes them like that, d'ye think?

— I used to say *Remember your badge*, and it worked like magic. I think if it hadn't been for the Sacred Heart, I don't know what would have happened.

— Ah, he was watching over you, so he was.

– So. And then ... So, one night I had to tell him. *I think we had better part.*

– Dear-a-dear-a-dear.

– I wasn't going to have any of that at all ... I never saw him from that day to this.

– Dear-a-dear. Ah, well, sure you were well rid of him.

– Well, I don't know. I sometimes think of him. We were very great, you know.

Later that night Bridget got the train back to her work in Glasgow. I carried her case and she gave me one and sixpence.

10

The Unemployed School at Battery Point. An old barracks that used to house a gunnery unit manning a cannon that covered the approaches to the Firth during the Great War. Now, only the concrete base remained of the gun. You went through the level crossing, turned right down the Inches Road past the Bath Rocks, the muck dump and the Flute Band hut, right down to the end past Christie's yard where the old ship-yard used to be and then you were at Battery Point, jutting out into the sea like a ship. Sometimes when it was rough the spray would come right over the school. And on a real stormy day of, say, gale force, you wouldn't be able to get there, the whole of Inches Road awash, the spray coming in steady streams like rain from the enormous waves thrashing against the Point, the school nearly submerged. That would be a great day, of course, you could spend it in the den where there was a good fire, listening to the rain on the big skylight. But days like that were few and far between.

Monday was one of the best days at the school – boxing first thing. Mister Hughes, the Gym teacher, makes a ring with ropes and there's a punch-bag and a punch-ball and we wear real boxing gloves and he lets us spar about then he will arrange a bout which we all watch. I sparred with Mick Cunningham, not the bus owners but the one who lives through the Buttercup Close. Mick is a very clever boxer, very fast and with a good punch. He has done some boxing before at Saint Mary's and his footwork is well worth watching, talk about Eleanor Powell. He's a good pal of mine and he was pulling his punches and just teaching me a few wrinkles about the game. Even then I got some digs and thumps for he is as hard as nails. Mister Hughes then arranged a bout between Wearie Nicolson and Spud Murphy, the fighting man of Stevenston. Nicolson put up a good show at the beginning but once Murphy had been hurt just once he tore right in to Nicolson and would have half-killed him if Mister Hughes hadn't stopped it. This Murphy can box, wrestle, lift weights and him not very tall, but broad. He is a holy terror in fact and a byeword around the Boglemart where nobody will go up against him. Anyway, that fight only lasted about five minutes and that was that. Then we had to clear away all the ropes and punch-balls and clobber.

Next, it was what they call *English*. Wee Mister Toner who lives up Montgomerie Street takes that as well as being the Head of the school as it's called. Some school. It's more like a reformatory. And we only go three days a week and then only in the mornings. That's enough, of course.

English means Mister Toner reading every week a bit from *Prester John*. Every week. *Prester John*. A book that goes on forever. Every week he gets this big stool out in the middle of the class-room, sits on it, looks up and says he will now continue with our English instruction, now where did he leave off last week. Then he goes on reading *Prester John*.

Anyway, when he was near to nodding off he stopped and then we continued with woodwork which is not all that bad. While there are a lot of cabinets and stands and all sorts of wooden knickery-knackery going on I can lose myself in

42

smoothing away at a drawer-knob while thinking dirty thoughts.

And then out. I had only a buttered roll to eat and this wasn't enough so I went over the rocks to gather some whulks. When I had a hankie full, I got an old tin from the dump, made a fire with driftwood, boiled the tin well to clean it, then boiled the whulks in sea water. I had as many of these as I could eat then wandered away through the old shipyard and then to the harbour where I hung around, whiling away the time till the Arran boat would come in and maybe somebody would want their bag carried.

There were only two boats in the big dock. One was a Spanish boat – the *Manuel Lopez* unloading iron ore and the other one the wee *Arran Mail*, a newly built coaster that takes the mail across to Arran and the papers on Sundays.

I went round to the lighthouse at the harbour entrance and watched some men fishing for mackerel at the end of the dock and wished I had a fishing line with me. I walked over to the rail right at the entrance itself, leaned over and dreamed at the sea bubbling at the base of the dock. If you stared down at the sea for long enough it would draw you in. But I had the rail to stop me, to hold on to. Once I had seen Barrell Clark sitting fishing on the end of the dock, a hot day, the sun dancing on the water, hypnotising, lean right over as if to get a closer look down through the green and splash he was in the water, very surprised, wondering how he had got there.

But you could lean over the rail, your legs wrapped around the upright and drowse away down at the sea without falling in. The breeze playing through your hair and the sun dancing in your eyes, you had a sense of motion as if on a ship. This same sea touched the shores of Arabia, of Africa, of Spain, America and some day you would sail out of this harbour on this same sea and away out past Arran and past Paddy's Milestone and past Ireland and out into the Atlantic and away.

Across from where you stood, the light-gantry on the break-water. Look right to Montgomerie Pier and beyond this to the left, the oil tanks of the Shell-Mex, then the beginning of the

43

North Shore, the sand dunes can be made out stretching away along the coast to Seamill, West Kilbride, Wemyss Bay and beyond. The houses of the big bugs along Eglinton Terrace and parallel, behind, those of the even bigger ones in Eglinton Road. Rising behind, the low hills, Dalry Road faintly visible running beside Knock Jardine where grass snakes can be found. Along the shore, moving dots of people. On the road a coal cart drawn up beside a gate, the baker's van, a pony and trap making its way along the road towards West Kilbride. Before the coast bends, opposite Montfode Farm you can just make out the rectangular wooden ice-cream hut of Agostini's. Big Aldo would be inside selling ice-cream sliders and double nougats and bottles of Ir'n Bru and Cola and Dandelion and Burdock Stout.

Look left, Arran towering, her head in the clouds, commanding the Firth, beyond her the Cumbraes and faintly in the distance, almost part of the sky, the Paps of Jura.

Someday...

Spotting the Arran boat approaching, I came out of my trance, left the rail, turned and, passing the mackerel fishers, walked over the cobbles past an old rusting crane, past the pilot house, across the bridge on the gate to the old dock – a couple of wee MacBrayne steamers tied up for overhaul – duking under the couplings of about four lines of railway wagons and came out at Winton Pier.

It was the new boat, the two-funnelled *Duchess of Hamilton* with a good crowd on board. But not many got off and those who did went straight on to the Glasgow train. They must have all been going on to Wemyss Bay or Dunoon. It was a dead loss.

I went home. There was nobody in but I got the key from its hiding place on a wee hook inside the jamb. I picked up a thick book and went over to the window to read it. Then the old lady came in.

– Oh, it's Patrick. You're home from the Unemployed School.

– Aye.

– What did you get today? It's getting you some work would

be more like it and you all running about and not knowing what to do with yourselves.

– English. But it's rotten. This wee man. He just reads out of a book every week.

– What book? Is it one of they big books?

– Yes. *Prester John* it's called. It's rotten. Naebody listens.

– It's not naebody. Can you not say nobody. Naebody.

– Nobody listens. And then we had woodwork.

– What are you making?

– Och, I don't like that. I'm making the same as I've always been making since we started.

– What's that?

– A drawer-knob.

– A what? A drawer-knob? And you've been doing that all this time?

– Ach well, ye know mammy ... You ... You never seem to be able to get it smooth enough. You know. I'm trying to get it ... You know ... So smooth you couldn't see my edges. You know what I mean?

– I'm sure I don't. It's a pity you couldn't have stayed on at school ... Went on to Saint Michael's College. If we could only have paid for it. If we'd only had the money.

– Aye, I know, mammy.

– And you such a good scholar too. Mister Scullion himself, the headmaster, said to me *Missus O'Connor, Patrick should go on you know. I'd like to see him going on, he has the brain.* Ah dear-a-dear. And him taking your compositions round the school too ...

– Aye, and half of the time he had me up for the strap. I don't like school, anyhow.

– Ah, dear-a-dear. And I thought ... An' I said to myself Patrick's going to be the great scholar, I said.

– I'd rather away to sea like my grandfather. It must be great to see all them foreign ports.

– Ah, keep off them oul' boats. Sure, they're no good till man nor beast ...

John and Annie came in together.

– Here's John and Annie, the only two that's working in the

family, if it wasn't for what Bridget sends us from Glasgow. That's not meaning anything to you, Patrick son ... Did any of you's two see your father at the corner?

– No, I didn't.

– No.

– And he promised to go with me to the pictures tonight. It's Victor MacLaglen in *The Informer*. A great picture about the troubles, who's this wrote the book? Liam O'Flaherty.

Annie said

– Mammy can I have some tea? I've got to be back over to the hotel as soon as I'm finished. All the visitors are down from Glasgow and the big bugs are giving them drinks.

She took off her coat. Underneath she had on her waitress's uniform and looked like a Lyon's Nippy with her white-ribbed apron, white black-braided cap tied round her hair, black throat-high dress under her apron, black shoes and stockings, all of which she was still paying for out of her wages.

– Here mammy, I've got some tips for you.

– That's a good wee girl, so you are. Here, sit down with me here and have a cup of tea.

– Are you finished with the motor, John?

I asked him.

– Aye, that's me finished for the day. He's learning me to drive.

– Are ye?

– Aye.

– Boys! I wish I could drive.

– Maybe I'll learn you sometime.

– Will ye? Boys!

The oldfella came in and Maggie greeted him with,

– Aye, there ye are.

– Aye. The same old sixpence. Muldoon, the solid man, as the poet says. Boys-a-boys, boys-a-boys.

– An' you were supposed to be taking me to the pictures tonight.

– Oh, that's right. Aye. Well, that's right. Sure, we're time enough, aren't we? Just give me a cup of tea and a jeely piece as the man said. Yis, I'll have a jeely piece, ha-ha ... Didn't I meet, d'ye know who I met at the corner?

— No.

— Dublin Dan. Yes, Dublin Dan, d'ye know? The Fenian. One of the real Fenians, d'ye know? He was in a flying column, so he was.

— Oh yis, is that right?

— Yis. Dublin Dan himself. A great old Fenian, so he is. And d'ye know ... he sails on the *Glencullen*. Ye know. Out and in to Dublin. Yes. He's a fireman on the *Glencullen*.

— Aye, well, take a cup of tea and there's a san'wich of slice sausage. It's Guthries, so it is.

— Yes. He sails in and out of Dublin. And who's this d'ye think he met in Dublin? Standing in the streets of Dublin. Says he, O'Connell Street, says he.

— We'll never be in time for the first house.

— What is this that's on?

— *The Informer.* And here a great many of the Irish players are in it, some of the Abbey actors are in it.

— Oh, is that so? Isn't that the great Liam O'Flaherty? I'd like to see the Abbey players again, so I would ... Yis. Standing outside the G.P.O. where your brother, God rest him, stood with the volunteers. Yes. Who d'ye think he met?

— No ... I couldn't tell ye.

— Uncle John from Cork. The same one. Yes ... And he's working in the Ford's motor works, so he is.

— Is that right, that's great. You'd better talk about it on the way to the pictures.

Annie was putting on her coat.

— I'm away, mammy.

— Aye, go on, hen. Watch yourself, now. And we'll see you tonight. We'll come and meet you at the corner.

— Aye, right. Ta-ta!

— Ta-ta!

— So long, kid!

shouted John. And I said

— Ah'll get ye!

— Oh, you's two, you're a right pair. Jak-Wes the Ape and Ben-The-House!

And then she was out the door. John shouted after her,

— Watch them Glasgow fellas don't get off with ye!

The oldfella went sailing on,

— Yes. In Ford's motor works. I believe he has the great good job, so he has.

Maggie was still trying to get him out.

— Yes, come on then, if you're ready.

— I wonder the now ... I was wondering if I was to write to him ...

— Come on then, here's your coat.

— Mind you, I haven't seen him for many's the long day.

He got up and began to put on his jacket.

— He would know oul' Dan, so he would. I never knew him to see you standing without the price of a pint.

As she handed Dan his cap, m'mother said to us,

— We're away to the pictures. Mind you and watch yourself, John, at that dance.

— Yes. All right.

— Yes ... If I got Patrick to write a letter for me ... If I was to send him a letter ... Ta-ta, son ... Johnny-I-Hardly-Knew-You. Yes, Johnny-I-Hardly-Knew-Ye ... Yes ... I wonder if there might not be a bit of a job for me, over there. I'd take you all back across the water ... Mind you, it's many a long year since—

And the rest was cut off by the door closing behind them. John said to me,

— What's the book?

— *The Blue Lagoon* by H. De Vere Stacpoole.

— Is it any good?

— It's soft.

— You canny beat Sax Rohmerr or Zane Grey.

— What about yourself? That book you were writing – *Jak-Wes the Ape*.

— Oh, yes.

He began to sing

— *Camerad – o!*

Camerad – o!

And then he made his voice trail away,

– *Camerad – o!*

He beat his chest. I said

– I like that bit. When Jak-Wes dies at the end, singing *Camerad – o.*

– I sent a story to the *Weekly News.*

– We'll see it in the paper.

– No.

He made a sad face.

– I never got any reply.

I joined my eyes with his in a sad look ... Then I said

– I'm away to meet Charlie Hands. Will you be wearing your pointed shoes?

– Yes.

– M'mammy will not let me get a pair.

– You're too wee yet.

– Och away! I'll be bigger than you, the now.

– Sez you.

– Yeh, sez me.

– And how.

– Said the monkey to the cow.

John getting dressed to go out was standing only in his simmit and trousers. He began to dance a fox-trot and sing

– *Turn on the heat, it's starting to drop,*
  Hubble and bubble, open the top,
  Hullo, it's forty below!
  If you are good, my little radiator,
  it's understood you'll get a gum-drop later,
  Turn on the heat, da-da-da-da ...

Humming to himself, he moved over to the looking-glass and began flexing his muscles in front of it. He turned to me and said

– Look at that muscle. Feel that muscle.

It certainly was some muscle. And it was like steel. Then there was a low sound like a girl's voice somewhere from outside going,

– Coo – ee!

John went over to the window, parted the curtains like someone in the pictures and keeked through. He made a sign

with his fingers and then in a kind of low yodel, went.
– O-oh! Oh-o!
What was he up to? I said to him again,
– I'm away, Jak-Wes.
– Ah'll get ye!
He came at me with his arms swinging like an ape but I was too quick for him. As I went down the stairs, Jeannie Aitken was standing on Boyle's landing looking suspicious. She paid no attention to me and I hung about the stone stairs to see what she would do. She slipped quietly up the wooden stairs and as she got to the top our door opened and I heard John saying
– It's all right, Jeannie. They're all away out,
before she was whipped through the door, quicker than Winkie.

Part 2 The mark of the beast

11

I was over at the window behind the orange box. M'father and mother sat by the fire with their faces up the chimley. M'mother said

– Oh, if only I had known the disgrace that was to be brought down on our heads, I would never have brought him into this world, God forgive me. Oh, I'm saying it. If I had only known. Oh, dear God. The troubles ... We get our share of troubles ... When I think of my mother, God rest her. Oh, it's just as well she's not here. Aye, it's just as well.

Dan took the pipe out of his mouth, spat into the fire and said

– Ah, maybe ... Maybe when all's said and done it would turn out not to be his at all. Sure, he denies it. It's maybe not his at all. There's been more than one there, I'm thinking. Jeannie Aitken wasn't born yesterday, you know. Sure, I've seen her galivanting about with them foreign sailors off the tankers, so I have. I've heard many's the tale about her, I could tell you many a tale about her.

– Aye, well she's going to claim him anyway ... You know what it was. I know what it was. We should never have left him in. That's what comes of leaving him in the house by himself.

– He's a grown man.

– Aye, grown man. Ye's are all alike. The mark of the beast ... Didn't my mother tell me? Yes, the mark of the beast. The dirt is in ye's.

– Well, it's the nature, ye see. The men can't go against their nature any more than a wumman can go against hers. When it comes to the bit, the man above made us the way we are.

– But it's the dirt. Our family were never dirty. There were never any dirty things in our lives.

– No, there was not, that's right.

– And you know that, don't ye? Dirty things that you couldn't talk about ... That a son of mine ... Oh ... That a son of mine would become a ... a ... a profligate, that's what he is. A bloody profligate, God forgive me.

– If it's him.

– If it's him, he's no son of mine. Ye'd better pray that it's not him. Aye, ye'd better pray ... Here's wee Annie. Come in hen and get some tea. What's up with you dear, you look as if you'd seen a ghost.

Annie had come in. She said

– Mammy, I'm frightened to come round the corner. They're all shouting at me from their windows. They're shouting about John.

– Are they, hen?

Dan said

– What the devil are they shouting about?

– They said *there's another one, look at her. Get your dirty brother to pay for his fun. Your brother's been up the close again. The dirty Irish.* And then they said a bad word. It's terrible. I've got to go back through them, forbye.

Maggie went on,

– Aye, it's terrible, all right. D'ye see that? D'y'see what the dirty devil has done for us? Never mind, Annie, you keep your head down, run by quick and never let on you hear them.

Dan said he would take her back round the corner. Annie said

– I'll give you my tips tonight, mammy.

– That's a great gerl. I'll put something bye for a coat for you.

– There's a nice one in Eddie Airds. The latest fashion.

– Aye, we'll have to get it from the wee man that comes round, dear. We'll go up to the warehouse and you can pick one out.

Annie was having some tea at the table.

– I hope they've got the fashion ... Mammy, Margaret Morgan's getting a permanent wave. Can I get one?

– Tt-tt-tt! Oh yes, time enough for that yet awhile. You're too young the now for that kind of thing. Tt-tt-tt! I think them things are awful fast. They're not right. You shouldn't be doing things to the hair that God gave you.

Annie keeked over at me.

– Look at our Patrick sitting over there. I hardly seen him. Where've you been today, Patrick? I suppose you've been in that old billiard hall.

– No, I haven't. I've been away looking for work.

– Where?

– The bottle factory in Irvine.

– Irvine?

– Aye, I got the lend of a bike.

– I'll have to away to the hotel. What would you be doing? Filling the bottles with I'r'n Bru?

– No, making them.

– Och, you couldn't make a bottle.

– Could I not?

M'father said

– Come on hen, I'll take you round the corner.

Annie went on,

– You'd be selling the bottles for pennies to spend in the billiard hall. I'll away.

I shouted after her,

– Ah'll get ye!

– Away, stoory heid,

she shouted back as she went through the door with the old-fella. M'mother said

– Were you looking for work, son?

– Yes. I got the lend of a bike and me and Charlie Hands went up to the bottle factory in Irvine. But we didn't have any luck. We went down the shipyard first to see if they needed anybody. But, as usual . . .

Then John came in. He looked hunted. Like the Sheriff was after him with his posse.

– Hullo, John. Here, did you—

– Don't be speaking to him! Don't say a word to him till he's seen your father.

He was in trouble. He said

– Any tea, mammy?

– Don't you mammy me. No, don't you mammy me. And I know the tea you'll get . . .

He went over to a corner of the window behind the press, drew the curtains and looked away out over the Firth in the vague direction of, say, the Klondyke.

– Yes, you'd better go over to the window. You'd better get out of my sight.

Dan re-entered and Maggie asked him if Annie was all right.

– Oh yes. Oh, there was nothing. I just walked past them and never let on, you know. There was a few of them muttering but I never minded.

M'mother then pointed the finger of scorn at John.

– Here he is. Here's the one that would bring disgrace on the house.

She went nearer to him till the finger was waggling under his nose.

– You know what they're saying in the street, don't you? And shouting out the windows at us? And Jeannie Aitken has come back home in the family way, throwing it up in our faces every time any one of us goes out? And she's saying it's yours? . . . Are you walking about with a mortal sin on your soul? Are you? Are you?

She didn't wait long enough for him to reply, going right on without taking a breath.

– Would you sit there under the picture of the Sacred Heart with the dirty things on your mind? Did you not learn your catechism at school? There's your catechism for you now. That's what you think of God's holy catechism ... And your sister Mary, God rest her, who's in heaven, looking down at you.

She looked for support to Dan who said
– For the sake of an oul' trollop who's running about with the sailors off the tankers. Are you a maan? Will you stand up and straight from the shoulder say it was your wean?

John just quietly said
– It's not mine.

Maggie pointed to the statue of the Sacred Heart.
– Will you swear before the wee red lamp that's burning in front of the Sacred Heart?

John didn't reply. M'father put in,
– Sure, what did you want to be running around with the likes of that for? Could you not have got someone better than that? I thought you were going to be better than that. With your pointed shoes and all your orders.
– Look at him. It's written all over his face. The mark is on his forehead, so it is. Oh, I see it. I can see the black mark on his forehead like a thumbprint ... Yes, the mark of Cain. The mark of the beast. The sin of adultery, God forgive me.

Dan was trying to calm her down a bit.
– Ah, maybe now, Maggie ... Maybe it would be—
– Do you know if you died this minute you would go straight down to the flames of hell where you would burn for all eternity? And your sister Mary a saint in heaven? Oh, she must be crying, she must be crying salt tears this night. Her salt tears will be raining down from heaven!
– Are you going to do like your mother asks you and swear in front of the wee lamp?

John seemed to study for a while and we all waited for his reply.
– No.

Maggie said
– You won't, will ye?

He studied again, then,
– No.

Inflamed by this even more, m'mother threw at him,

— If you don't then you know where you'll go m'boy. Do you know where you'll go? Eh? Do you know where you'll go?

— No.

— You'll march out to the priest in the chapel with me. You'll march out to Father Reilly and get down on your bended knees in front of the Blessed Sacrament of the altar and take a holy oath that that child is not yours!

This was some months after I had seen John whipping Jeannie Aitken into the attic. After being away in the North of Scotland she had just re-appeared in Harbour Place and she was up the cookie.

12

And John was being claimed as the father. So we were in trouble.

I knew about it straight away as I went into the Unemployed School. Yaller Kennedy came over and said

— Has your brother been up the close again?

— If it was any of your business I would tell you.

— I bet he's been up the close again.

— Away. You couldn't get up the Cannon Hill, never mind the close.

Then he and two cronies began to sing

— *Johnny will you give over telling the tale to me,*

Telling the tale to me,

Oh, telling the tale to me.

I will have a baby, the father you will be,

If you don't give over telling the tale to me,

Seven and six you'll have to pay

For coming up the close with me.

I didn't let that worry me. I just asked them if they were jealous. Anyway, John was denying it so I could just stick up for him and deny it as well.

That was a good day in the Unemployed School. The day we overthrew Prester John.

As soon as the wee man brought out his high stool and we saw him getting the book there was the loudest and longest groan ever heard in the class. And, as he mouthed the first words, everybody began to put their heads in their arms and make snoring noises. Then Wearie Nicolson threw up his arms as if he was shot and slumped in his seat. Soon, everybody in the class-room was doing the same thing until the place was covered with bodies.

– Stop this. Stop this at once!

the wee man shouted at us.

– Ah-rr-gch-gch!

was the answer from every corner.

He approached the first row, put his hand under Tommy Wilson's arm and half-lifted, half-cajoled him to an upright position. He went along the row doing the same thing to the rest.

– This is English reading. You must pay attention. It is for the betterment of your mind. It will help you to get a good job in the world.

Sez him. As he got to the second row, the first slumped again, the bodies in turn one after the other throwing up their arms and groaning.

– This will not do. Boys! Boys!

Spud Murphy splattered Jimmy Anderson with an ink pellet.

– Who did that!

Mister Toner wheeled round. While he peered at the back, Tommy Wilson stuck out his leg and knocked the book, which had been left on the stool, on to the floor. Mister Toner wheeled to the front again.

– Come out the boy who did that!

Whichever way Mister Toner turned, someone started something behind his back. Spud Murphy and Wearie Nicolson began to fence with rulers. They stood up. Mister Toner rushed to separate them. While he was trying to do this another fencing match started behind him. I began to fence with Charlie Hands. Wearie Nicolson backed out on to the floor pursued by Spud – Prisoner of Zenda – Murphy knocking over the stool as they went. Everybody began to stand up on the seats.

– Hungah! Hungah!

some shouted in unison. Jimmy Anderson climbed up on the big window sill, lifted the watering-can and sprayed those underneath with it. Mister Toner, his face getting redder, began to rush hither and thither stopping fights. His hair, which only grew round the sides was hanging down his forehead in wisps and strands. But every pair he stopped from fighting just started up again as soon as he had turned his back.

– Boys! Boys! Play the game, boys!

Spud Murphy having run through Wearie Nicolson till he was fed up with it now led him in a dance round the floor. He was soon joined by the rest of the class, each one holding on to the boy in front until there was a chain going all round the room. Of course, Mister Toner got himself in the centre like he was het.

– *Tarry-um-a-dee,*
  The monkeys up the tree,
  Ate all the coconuts
  And left nane for me!

The class-room was jumping. The din, deafening.

– Hungah! Hungah!

Some shouted at Mister Toner,

– Tig, you're het!

The chain weaved in towards him and out again, boys giving him a pat as went past. He was jostled from side to side.

– Boys, I appeal to you!

Without warning, Murphy led the chain out into the corridor with the teacher after him. Finding the door open at the end, Murphy went straight out, the rest following. When we got out into the open, the smell of freedom tanged by the sea took our heads and, led by Murphy, we all, with one will ran off down the Inches Road, leaping in the air, shouting *Hungah!* pushing, shoving, punching. Soon the whole class, that is, the entire school was running down the road, all of us with one idea, to get as far away from Prester John as possible. We left the figure of Mister Toner standing outside the school door, waving his arms, shouting, his figure and his voice becoming smaller and smaller.

– Come back! Come back! Boys, come back!

That is how we overthrew Prester John.

A good number of us went to the Inches Road rubbish dump, made a fire and boiled whulks. The out-of-towners disappeared early, back to their own territory and I and a few others wandered over to watch an unemployed's pontoon school behind the flute band hut. Blin' Jock Macready, the leader of the band, was in the bank and winning. Some of the bigfellas standing watching began to take a rise out of us.

– You should all be in school. You're not old enough to watch big games.

– Away!

– There's wee Connor.

– How's your brother, the Hooker-Down?

– He'll hook you down.

– Aye, he hooked that wee lassie down, I hear.

– Ha-ha-ha.

– Aye, he was there.

– Is that his wee brother?

– What age are you, son?

– Old enough.

– He's not sixteen. Are you sixteen?

– I have to be sixteen to go to the blinkin' Unemployed School.

– Here, you better watch that language.

– Sixteen. Can you come yet? You can come when you're sixteen, you know.

– Have you not tried it yet on your wee robin?

– His brother can come all right.

– He tried it all right.

– Ha-ha-ha.

– This one's too wee for sixteen.

– What size is it, wee fella.

– Ach, away.

– Get your wee robin out and pull it up and down and you'll wonder what's happening to you.

– Watch you don't have a wet dream.

– Don't make a mess of your mother's blankets.

– Ha-ha-ha.

They were a right lot of hard cases. We left them to the game. Some of us wandered over the Bath Rocks, along to the promenade and up the steps in front of the Barony Church, round to the Transport bus station. A bus came in from Glasgow and Tommy Wilson got a lucky carry. Only three people got off but one woman was going up to Seton Street with a heavy case. So he was all right. I said ta-ta to the rest and turned into Bute Place, heading home.

Mister Slicer was putting the padlock on the gate of the Church of the Nazarene after cleaning it out. Crossing over to number nine, our close, I saw a knot of women beside the big pen. As I neared them, the knot opened and there was Jeannie Aitken in the centre. She shouted

– Aye, you're lookin'. You can tell your big brother it won't be long now, so you can.

And shouts came from the window-leaners on all sides.

– That's right, Jeannie!

– The poor wee lassie.

– He can't deny it! Let him try to deny it!

But number nine is at the near end so I didn't have to walk through them or travel very far before the close swallowed me up.

Nobody in. Take a chance, pull the old gramophone – *Decca* – out from underneath the bed and put on a record. Not supposed to play it by yourself, only when all the family sit round on a Sunday night to listen. John McCormack. Grace Moore. Lawrence Tibbet. Go through a pile of Woolworth records sixpence each and some second-hand ones bought in Jerusalem, Glasgow. *All Among the Barley – The Gypsy Accordion Band. I Saw Three Ships – The Famous Westminster Choir. Old Birthday Cards.* Tenor solo by *Richard Churchman.*

    Old birthday cards,
    Old birthday cards,
    Bygone memories bringing,
    Friendships fragrant to them clinging.
    Wishes sincere, love and regards.
    They bring a sigh of years long gone bye,
    Those old birthday cards.

It's my Mother's Birthday Today, the sensational boy singer *Master Joe Peterson.* Put on *Zonophone* record *The Wedding of the Painted Doll – Jack Payne and his Famous Band.*

Walk to the window. Da-ra-ra-ra-da, da-ra, da-ra, pattern on the oilcloth syncopating. The shunting yard. Train going past. Trucks. To where? Ride the rods buddy. Jump a train and head out West. Become a hobo. Adventures. Hitting this town walking down the main street. Stranger. Here, buster. Here, Scotty. Whap! By God that gringo could handle himself. See the way he threw the Mexican over his head. Silence as you enter the saloon. Dangerous Dan Mulgrew. A bunch of the boys were whooping it up. In a marmalade saloon. Bunk in the yard a train leaving in the morning. Good morning blues. Freight train. Waa. Waa-Waa. The Atchinson, Topeka and Santa Fe. Heading West. The rods again. Riding. Riding. A ride. Are you sixteen yet. Can you ride? What is it like to have a ride. You think a ride it makes it come up. Take off the record and put the gramophone away. Quick. You did it. Shove back under the bed. As you bend down it gets in the way. It's up. Stick it up. Back to the window. Look across to Herald Street you can see the windows. Keek from behind the curtains maybe you can see a girl pulling her clothes up. Maybe you could see her bare naked. Are you sixteen yet. Can you come. No, I'm going somewhere else. Try it on your wee robin. What do you do. A ride. Ride up and down like on horseback. Take it out. Swelling. The top of it hurts. It wants to burst out. A mouth like a serpent behind another bigger mouth which is stretched tight. Ride. Atchinson, Topeka and Sante Fe. Lie down on bed behind the curtains. If anybody comes in you can put it back. Stiff. Robin. Here's my hand on it. *True Confessions*. Love life of the stars. *Photoplay*. The Brown Derby. Seen around town. Jean Harlow is being squired around town by Patrick O'Connor. She is thrusting under your hand. She hurts. Grip it. Get a grip on yourself. You're touchy. Itchy. Annie in her pink silk knickers. Celanese. A darker shadowed vee. Pull your stockings up I can see your fancy garters. Up. Up the close. At the top of the close I saw your pussy licking milk. Pink lacy garters. *I was a good time girl*. Thrown back on sofa her skirt comes up showing frilly petticoats. *Improve Your Bust*. Send for amazing booklet. Nothing to pay. When you slide your hand down it jumps. Jean Harlow leans forward you can see down between her tits. Touch the page. Can you feel her. Get a feel up the close. Next time with the gang. Take them up the close pull their knickers down. In the dark. Squealing. Something soft you stick your fingers in. Squeal. *The Picture Show*. Waa. Waa-Waa. That's the Broadway Melody. Hold. What did they say pull up and down as if you didn't know. Constant Cummings. Up and down. Busby Berkely. Legs of the chorus girls dance together kicking up. See up to the top. If you could only lie down on the stage and look up. When they kick. When they open. Up and down. Itchier and itchier. To their bums. *New Slimfit Corsets for that Trim Figure*. Attached by elastic to a belt that stretches over thighs and buttons on to stockings. Oh. The elastic stretches tight but you must stretch harder. Pull harder. You can't stop. The train don't stop here bud. Non-Stop. The Chieftain. Pulls out. Pull. Heaven opens a pussy paws. And pull. Terrible itch to scratch you must go on and a thrill garters scooshing and jumping you'll wonder what's happening to you.

I never knew you had it in you.

Silver shining wonders will never cease.

When Annie came in that night she said there had been shout-

ing and things being called at her in the street.
−They were shouting *When's your brother going to own his wean* and *That's all they Fenians are good for.* Some of them shouted out the windows and shook their fists.

The oldfella said
−Never mind them. Never you mind them. They're only out for trouble. Sure, they're only a lot of oul' ra-has anyway, a lot of oul ra-has.

John didn't come in till very late, till everybody was in bed. Maggie and Dan had stayed up for a long time talking in whispers at the fireside before finally putting out the lamp and going to bed. John crept in when everyone was asleep. But I had stayed awake, keeking through the curtains of the set-in bed at the moon lighting the floor near the window and listening. I heard the Belfast boat blowing at midnight and then another two ships passing far away out on the Firth before I heard his foot quietly on the stair. As he climbed in beside me I said
−Good old Jak-Wes,
to let him know I was on his side. He put his finger up to his lips but he squeezed my shoulder. We cooried up back to back.

13

During the day John kept out of trouble by staying away. Anyway, he was on Jimmy Stewart's motor most of the time and even there he used to come in for some taunts if any of Jeannie Aitken's kin was on it. He would rise in the morning at the crack of dawn and get the rolls from Murchie's bakehouse before anybody was out. After having his breakfast he would shin over the back wall into Missus Cosgrove's yard, climb the wall to the railway shunting yard, cross this at a run − the boat trains come through here and McTavish, the big railway dud would lift you if he nabbed you – a walk along the shore and so by the back way to the motor stand. As I ate my rolls which were still hot there was no sign of him. I was up early as there was an auction on at McKellar's furniture sale-room. There were always a few odd lots that the regular cart couldn't handle which old McKellar would let us deliver on a barrow for what we could get.

Tommy Wilson was mating with me that day and we met at the corner and went round the yard at the back of the Eglinton Hotel to take a lend of the barrow. The hotel barrow was bigger than the railway one but you had to be up early to nab it before anybody else.

– *As I went down the Boglemart*
I met wee Jimmy O'Hara.
He ses if ye gi'e' me a suck o' your rock
I'll gi'e' ye a hurl o' m' barra.
Oh, the bonny wee barra's mine,
It didna belong to O'Hara,
But the fly wee Jock – He stuck to m' rock
And I'm gonna stick t' the barra!

A couple of choruses of this, which Tommy couldn't sing very well because of always coughing with his bad chest, brought us to outside the sale-room. We sat on the windowsill of the Castle Hill Vaults back room to wait for the opening, sharing a good-sized Gold Flake ciggy Tommy had picked up outside the hotel which didn't have much of a mouth on it. After that we strolled down to the Lyric corner, not going too far away and keeping an eye on the barrow in case of proguers.

The Lyric was the former flea palace known as the Princes Picture House before it went over to the talkies. In a transformation scene which was the talk of the wash-house for weeks, it was decorated in pastel colours inside and out, given a new gold velvet curtain, an electric sign outside and big Andy Smyllie in a musical comedy uniform to keep the weans in order.

Gads, an English picture again. *A Lansborough Film.* We couldn't see the names as they were just being put up but on the photos outside there was a horsy-faced woman and her rotten dog standing outside a church talking to a daft-looking minister. But there was a Charlie Chase comedy short, a Mickey Mouse cartoon and the Gaumont-British Newsreel.

The sale-room doors were open and people were beginning to crowd in early to get the bargains. Soon, they would be overflowing on to the pavement as there wasn't all that much room inside. Every inch of space was crammed with grandfather clocks, tallboys, dressers, mirrors, wardrobes, washstands and every sort of furniture.

Mister McKellar climbed up on a stand like a pulpit.

– ... eight shillings are you done now eight shillings – eight shillings will anyone make it nine shillings – you madame thank you for nine shillings – the lovely mahogany wash-stand – nine shillings I'm bid now nine shillings – nine shillings any advance on nine shillings – nine shillings are you done now nine shillings – for the first time nine shillings are you done now nine shillings – for the second time are you done now nine shillings – for the third time nine shillings for the lovely mahogany wash-stand – sold to the lady on my right for nine shillings.

At the end of the sale, the only job that was left out of the regular deliveries was a wardrobe to be taken to West Kilbride. But that was about five miles away, up several braes at that, a fair job for a horse and cart or a motor lorry, no job for a hand-cart.

We took it.

Mister McKellar said

– Well, if you can manage it, son, you're welcome to take it on. I need it delivered the night to a wumman who has letting-folk coming down from Glasgow. And the motor's booked up and the cart, away. There's seven shillings in it from me and whatever the wumman gives you after you've done it.

We lashed the wardrobe on to the big square barrow and away with it, short-cutting down side streets till we got to the North Shore by way of the brae at the top of Montgomerie Street. This was our first hard pull, we had to both get behind it, dig our feet in and shoving, struggle every inch of the way to the top – a kind of dress rehearsal for the big brae at West

Kilbride. Poor old Tommy was peghing away for every breath by the time we got to the top. And then it was nearly as much of a struggle to hold it back going down the other side. Along Eglinton Terrace, round by the greasy pole past Agostini's ice-cream hut – a wave to Amalia who was serving – then we were faced with the long haul along the wind-swept shore road with the Firth on our left and the fields on our right. Still, there was Arran to look at as we trudged along and it was at its best, cloud and sun producing a continued picture of changing colours when suddenly a glen, unseen before, would be illuminated between a cleft in the mountains and a stream would flash silver. It would be great to be there only it was a stamping ground mostly for big bugs. They say Jack Buchanan goes there for his holidays. You can see him sometimes catching the *Glen Sannox*.

The star of this continued picture was Patrick O'Connor, also featuring Tommy Wilson, journeying into the Wild West Kilbride with a covered wagon loaded with essentials for the fort of a small bunch of pioneers who were holding out to the last man against a tribe of Possilpark Peyotes.

The milkman from Montfode Dairy passed us, standing up on his cart and driving his horse like Ben Hur, the sun glinting on the brasswork of the cans and wheel-hubs, a lovely wee cart if there ever was one and a fine well groomed horse forbye, its coat, as everything else, polished like a new pin. We gave him a cheer as he went past and he saluted with his whip.

Tommy Wilson began to tell me about the punt he gets the lend of some Sundays from Wullie Lundie who drives the Pilot Boat and builds boats in his spare time in a shed down the Inches. Wullie lets him take out this punt on a Sunday when he has to work a shift. Sometimes Eesky Dan Huggins comes with him and they row the boat to the Horse Island which is just a strip of land not far outside the break-water. But it is a good place for birdsnesting, fishing and catapulting seagulls. There is plenty of driftwood for a fire and plenty of mussels to boil on it. He asked me if I could row and I said of course so he said I could take an oar some Sunday and row the boat out with him and I jumped at the chance. The punt is moored down the old dock not far from the Pilot House and it would be a great way to plunk Mass of a Sunday.

I thought I spotted a familiar shape on the horizon.

– Here, there's the *Juno*.

– Where?

– Just coming round the Big Cumbrae.

– No, it is not.

– It is, look, see the spray of the paddles? You can only just see it. The spray wouldn't be there if it was propeller-driven. And the water would be different.

– Aye. I think you're right. It might be the *Juno*. I think it is. Yes, you might be right.

– It's the *Juno* all right.

– Mind it used to run into Ardrossan?

– Yes, I mind it fine.

– Where's it running now?

– I think it's running between Largs and Dunoon.

– Look, it's fairly going its dinger. Not like me. I'm getting puffed out.

– So am I.

– C'mon, we'll take a rest, eh?

– Aye, c'mon.

Although we had been keeping the crack going all the time and there was plenty to look at, the load was getting harder and harder to push and our feet were scuffling more and more. We would probably waste more boot leather than could be paid for from what we would get. Tommy was coughing again. He said

– Do you think we will ever get there?

– I think we were daft to try it.

– I had to. There's not a penny in the house. And we've pawned nearly everything.

– We've a few bob coming in. But not much.

– At least m'mother will be able to get something the night.

– If we get back the night!

– We better keep on.

We were lying down on the dunes of the North Shore. I said

– Who ever heard of anybody taking a wardrobe from Ard-rossan to West Kilbride on a *handcart*?

– And we're not a quarter of the way yet.

– And don't forget the brae we've got to get up.

At the thought we both burst into laughing, the funny side was too much for us. But poor Tommy finished his laugh with a worse cough than ever. Even so, as soon as he got his wind he said

– Ach well, we'd better come on if m'mother is to get us fish suppers this night.

– You might get tuppence worth of chips out of it, ha-ha.

There wasn't anywhere you could get a drink between Ago-stini's hut and Seamill at the foot of the big brae and by the time we got there we could have been in the Sahara desert we were so parched. Tommy looked in a bad way, all the colour had drained from his face.

After a rest, we tackled the brae but before five yards we found it was taking all our strength to keep it from running back again, never mind getting it up. We were drenched in sweat, parched, on our last legs, and the brae stretched away up ahead of us for miles and miles, it looked.

About level with a coal cart, we were sitting on the shafts of the barrow wondering if we could get Jak-Wes the Ape or maybe Samson at short notice to get us up the brae when the coalman who was with the cart came strolling over to us.

– Where d'ye think ye're goin' with that barra?

We told him.

– Where've ye come from?

We told him.

– Ye didnae!

We did.

His black face broke into a grin that would have put Al Jolson on second billing.

– Well, that beats them a' ... Here ... Wait till I get m'horse backed round and you'll not see what I'll do wi' ye.

Not only did he get a rope, hitch the barrow on to the cart and pull it up the hill with us holding on to the shafts but he helped us to hold it back going down the other side. Looking at

his black face, I felt like breaking into a Christie Minstrel song but instead, as we went down the hill, we gave him another chorus of,
– *Oh, the bonny wee barra's mine,*
  It didnae belong to O'Hara,
  But the fly wee jock, he stuck to m'rock
  And I'm gonna stick to the barra!

The coalman, leaving us at the foot of the hill and going back to his horse, said
– If that doesn't beat the ban'. I never thought you young fellas had it in you.

All we had to do then was to wheel the barrow along a bit to the house which was near the bottom of the brae and we soon got the wardrobe inside and standing where the woman wanted it. After that, I went into the back kitchen to get a drink of water. While I was having this I heard a shout and the sound of running feet in a bit of a confloption. When I went back in, Tommy was lying stretched out on the sofa, unconscious, his face bluer than ever. The woman's son had run out for the doctor.

The ambulance took him straight to the hospital. The woman was nearly crying as she gave me seven shillings and sixpence and her son helped me up to the top of the brae with the barrow. I pushed it home by myself but that seemed easy after the outward journey. I bought a penny pop and had a good slug first. McKellar's saleroom was just closing as I got there and they gave me the seven shillings for the job. I ran straight round to Missus Wilson and gave her seven and six. The polis had already been to tell her about Tommy and all the weans were crying but her face lit up when I gave her the money and told her it was from Tommy. She thanked me and sent one of her boys straight out to Coyle's fish and chip shop.

I got a right row when I took the barrow back to the Eglinton Hotel. The Boots had been searching all over the town for it and the manager threatened everything from blue murder to the polis for keeping the barrow out all day but he knew me through my sister working there for a while and I got away with it.

14

Although she had been wondering about my being away for so long without coming in to get something to eat all day, m'mother was quite pleased when I gave her five shillings from what I had earned, telling her I was keeping sixpence to myself. She looked at me, as usual making it clear she didn't believe a word of it, and saying she warranted I was keeping a shilling to myself but I stuck to my guns and that meant I skinned her for one and sixpence, making two bob in all. So that was me for the pictures the next night. There was a good gangster film in the Countess, *The Petrified Forest* with a new actor, Humphrey Bogart, a very funny name for a gangster, surely, not like Edward G. Robinson or James Cagney.

Poor old John was still creeping in late at night and keeping out of the way as much as possible but m'mother had not followed up her threat to take him in front of the priest yet. I heard her saying to the oldfella that, as the wean was not born, there was not much Jeannie Aitken or her family could do and he said when it was born and if she proved it was his, John would have to pay seven and sixpence a week to keep it. There was no question of them getting married, of course, because Jeannie was a protestant, not on your Nellie Duff, no holy water in the Orange Lodge.

So John would just sit like Mump Chants over by the window and nobody was allowed to speak to him, his only friend Zane Grey and sometimes Jack London. Whenever we got the chance, though, he and I would have a chinwag and anyway he well knew that I was on his side. I looked up to him. I hadn't had a ride yet.

Jeannie Aitken was plump and dark. She wore a fringe across her forehead and a right cheeky look on her face. Before she was put up the cookie she was always giggling a lot and screeching and being chased by the men. The talk was that she was a good thing. She'd been seen with sailors and around

70

our way that made her a whoor anyway even if she had only been trying to convert them.

I wonder what it was like? If John had been there, he knew. I had seen him anyway when he was getting out of bed stepping over me, his shirt tail flapping open and I looked up to see red wrinkled covered in hair swingers swivelling two great ones like footballs swelling and his tosshel swaying semi-hard before he grabbed his shirt front and covered himself, gripping the tail between his legs. Still bulging through the khaki shirt. He looked surprised when he saw I was awake and I could see his eyes thinking I wonder if he saw it because it wasn't right down. He must be like me and wake up with it rock-hard every morning.

If he did it to Jeannie Aitken, I wonder where? That night I saw her being pulled into the attic. Did he put her on top of the big bed or in behind the curtains of the set-in bed. Or against the coalhouse door. Or over the table. Did he take off her knickers. What does it look like. That must have been it last week when me and five other fellas dragged Rosie Wilson, Bessie's sister, up Henderson's close in fun. She was squealing but you couldn't see anything in the dark and all the hands were groping, all trying to make contact. She was down on the ground and her skirt was up the hands were pulling at the elastic of her knickers and you could feel all the hands and then a soft leg in the pitch darkness and then fingers and something even softer your fingers sinking in and it was spongy and soft and your fingers afterwards were a bit moist.

I went downstairs to the yard and up to the lavatory, the only place you could be by yourself unless you were in the house with nobody else in.

I stand, my trousers already swelling there is this force it will not be kept down. Almost no time to get it out. The force of it. Like a gun. The force of a bullet. The loveliest feeling you ever had in your life. If it is like that by yourself what must a ride be like? I wish I could get one.

After planking a shilling under the oilcoth over by the window for the pictures and a tuppeny packet of Woodbines, I had another one left, enough for two games at six or two.

I'll have you,
Six or two,
I'll have you,
It's a sin to tell a lie.

So it was the den for me again, nice and early, across Princes Place, wee Red Joe still there bumming his chat to an audience of do'es that strutted around pecking and ooklacooing to him that they didn't believe a word.

– Aye, it will not be long now till yon brother of yours'll be a faither,

he said to me, removing the aged stump of yellowed clay pipe from his face and, from the side of his mouth, aiming a tobacco goggle at the nearest pigeon.

I girned at him,

– Do you live at this corner? They should cast you in stooky and put palings around you.

That would hold him for a while.

The den was not empty, the top table was on, two learners with a set of snooker but Tam was playing his gramophone. I recognised the voice straight away.

– *I'm growing fonder of every star,*
I love to wander where daises are.
Is it a wonder, I'm growing fonder of you?

And then a break on the piano. Tam turned to me as I came in and our eyes hit the roof together in appreciation of the maestro himself, *Fats*.

Then we harmonised a bit along with the record.

– *I'm growing fonder of everything,*
I love to wander in the woods in spring.
Is it a wonder I'm growing fonder of you?

The tinkling of his keys was like the whistling of the birds in the woods in spring of the song, the fat man skipping through the honkytonk trees, the den filled with the joys of sprung rhythm.

But all this had to end.

It was very early and I still had to go to the Unemployed School which didn't begin until eleven o'clock.

Mister Toner peered over his spectacles as if he was trying to find out if the class was in a good mood and prepared to stay for the lessons.

There had not been much said about our bolting the week previously. Mister Hughes had given us all a lecture on good sportsmanship and he kept talking about playing the game with your headmaster, not giving up the ship, never deserting your post, staying till the bugle sounded retreat, standing by the captain, you would have thought we were in the Foreign Legion, but no such luck it was only the Burroo School.

But, as the whole school had plunked it together, there was not much they could do about it. They could hardly expel the entire school or Mister Toner and Mister Hughes would be signing on the Burro themselves and that would be a fine how-d'ye-do.

Mister Toner spoke softly.

– I have decided to introduce a new book into English reading. A more up-to-date book. One more in keeping with the times. One which, I am sure, will inspire you to go out and do great deeds in the world and get on. *Ivanhoe* by Sir Walter Scott.

He paused to see the effect this announcement was having on us but the thick atmosphere was disturbed only by a loud resonant cracking sound. He decided to ignore this and the guffaws that arose on all sides and went to get his stool.

Ivanhoe. Spud Murphy leaned over and whispered to me,

– Hi, Connor. You're a great one for reading. Is this Ivan Hoe a Rooshian book?

I kidded him on.

– Yes. It's about the cossacks.

– That should be all right.

Somebody said

– That smell's not all right. Who did that?

– It's a right Rooshian smell that.

Murphy said

– It must have been Ivan Hoe.

Michael Cunningham said

– No, it was Wearie. He was drinking Rooshian stout in the Cross Keys on Saturday night.

The class collapsed again at this. Mister Toner busied himself in a cupboard searching for the book or keeping well out of the way. When the laugh died down a bit, Spud Murphy kept it on by saying

– If you ask me it was the man with the blue arseole.

Wearie laughed so much at this that he gave vent to another cracker. Those of us sitting near to him began to clear a space around him. Mister Toner approached.

– Now boys, what's this, what's this! You don't need to be leaving your seats.

– Sir, it's terrible.

– You would leave your seat as well, if it was you.

– Sir, even Ivan Hoe couldn't stand it.

– Sir, that one came out in its Rooshian boots.

Charlie Hands picked up a jotter-book and began fanning the air around Wearie. When the air was breathable again and we had taken our seats, Wearie said

– I suppose this Ivan Hoe's a fermer. Please sir, does the hoe mean that he's a fermer?

An unknown voice was heard distinctly saying

– All that fughin Stevenston crowd are fermers.

If Mister Toner heard this he made no sign but said

– It's *farmer* not *fermer* and Ivanhoe was not a fermer but a warrior. He should inspire in you how to fight life's battles in the world and get on and land a good job.

So I said to myself, like all the rest of us I suppose, I'd better listen to this for a while and see what it's all about and if it's any good and that is why it was quiet for fifteen minutes that day.

15

– Does he know? Where's the playboy? Out in the motor, I suppose. Did ye hear the latest? D'ye know what Missus Morgan's just after saying to me? D'ye know?

Maggie aimed these words at the oldfella sitting by the fire reading his *Noon Record* for winners. He looked up.

– No. What was it you were hearing?

– Thats ... D'ye know what I've just been told? D'ye know what she was telling me?

– Has she been giving you—

– Jeannie Aitken ...

– Jeannie Aitken. And what's this—

– She's away. That's her away.

– I wonder if—

– Thursday night. That's her going to have it now. She's away to the hospital to have it now. She went away on Thursday night. I thought it was a bit quiet.

– Aye, well maybe it will be quiet for a while. Maybe we'll get some peace for a while now.

– Yes. Ah, well. Aye, and we'll soon know now. We'll know now all right. Wait till she comes out.

– Ah – hah!

– We'll see some fun then, so we will.

It was a Saturday afternoon and I heard this before leaving for the den. So, she was away to the hospital to have her wean and I suppose poor old John would be biting his nails to see what would happen but at least it would be a bit quieter while everybody in the street waited for the next instalment.

The Saturday smell – cut up Hill Street and past Missus Rae's Bar and out the door the strong beer fumes – you can see a crowd of men just inside the door a haze of tobacco smoke above their bunnets – look at Mary Barbour's shop window as you go past – on this side Ogden's Four Square tobacco War Horse plug a tin poster on the front of the shop white enamel with blue letters Players Please – little wooden

bowls of shag – a large black twist of tobacco hanging on a nail
– when you go in for a half-ounce of tobacco for the oldfella
Mary Barbour takes the plug and cuts it on the counter under
a tobacco cutter then weighs it on the brass scales always
throwing in a wee bit to make up a good measure – turn the
corner the other window is full of toys you see a box of ludo as
you pass quickly – but here is big Alec Ballantyne standing
right at the corner swaying with a beer bottle sticking out of his
pocket – hullo, Alec – go on looking at the gutter Swan Vestas
matches kick a Gold Flake box off the pavement – past the
gates of the railway goods yard which is where the bonny wee
barrow is poghled from if somebody has not been there before
you – the green cast-iron *Gentlemen's Urinal* all the iron work
wrought into designs heads of angels spears fishes leaves – the
salty smell of pee meeting you as you turn the corner – the
billboards with strips torn off you tear it further as you go past
A.1. Soap Powder – *Bovril prevents that sinking feeling* the
wee red-haired man in his pyjamas – *Scott's porridge oats* a
kiltie tossing a big caber then at the bottom scrawled in pencil *I
can see your bum Betty Foran* along a bit *Alec luvs Black
Maggie* along a bit *Prick* a bit further *Shite* – across the road
past McKellar's salesrooms you remember that day with the
big wardrobe on the Eglinton barrow – Sanny Taylor outside
the *Castle Hill Vaults* talking to Blin' Jock the big drummer
and leader of the Winton Flute Band well Sanny plays Centre-
Forward for Winton Rovers I wonder if he will score any
goals today against Irvine Meadow Eleven – Hullo Sanny –
along Hill Place – Missus Norwood is leaning out her window
looking at you I wonder if they know up here about Jeannie
Aitken – past the close where Jimmy Morrison's cousin who
has just got married got a room and kitchen but they had a
terrible job to get rid of the bugs – past P. Marron's wee shop –
a few weans pressing their faces against the window wondering
what to buy it's a great place for ogie-pogie eyes – Peter Smith
has started a book taking lines outside the *Horse-Shoe Bar* –
Wullie Brannif standing there with Big Eddie McGinn the
bo's'un who sailed to the frozen North with the *Bay Rupert* for
the Hudson Bay Company and was stranded on the ice –

Hullo Wullie – in Kilmahew Place is another bookie lifting lines and a few men studying the paper outside *Coyle's Fish and Chip Shop* – Gudge McGurk shuttles back and forth from the bookie to the den to the *Ship Bar* – Hullo Gudge – turn into Glasgow Street very busy with A.1. buses and Transport services the Co-Operative coal cart goes past and Lees lemonade lorry overtakes it – cross the street past *Starks* where we get the *Weekly News* and *The Startler* on tick – around the *Ship Bar* corner through the crowd standing there – Hullo Josie Hullo Steve Hullo Ben – past the wee dairy and into the den.

You feel the usual kick deep in your stomach as the smell of chalk and cigarettes and the electricity from the friction of the balls surrounds you. No gramophone or guitar or Bing or Fats Waller on Saturday the big day but the nerve-string music with heart-thump rhythm accompaniment from winners and losers staking their last tanners on snooker or five-pin pool

Chooky Templeton is here yes he looks up this has been coming for some time he is going to challenge you it is a good level game you think you can beat him on form. He grins you see the light coming in to his eyes he thinks he can beat you he shouts hi Pat I'll have you for the table and a shilling at snooker. You say level. He says you could give me a start trying to conn but I'll play you level one set a shilling and we'll

Tam lets you take the balls from the office yourself he gives you a pally grin and allows you the new set. You put up the pyramid of reds the black behind it the pink just in front touching the point of the triangle the blue on the centre spot yellow brown green on the three spots of the dee making sure

toss for break he breaks plays the ball back round to the dee leaving nothing on. You play it thin off the hardly-broke pyramid and off the back cush back to safety again. He tries for one near the top cush misses and leaves one over the middle bag. You pot this you go for the brown you pot that five in the game striker up you miss the next red. He pots a red a green another red a pink misses the next red. Your turn to play six in the game striker down. You pot a red a yellow a red a blue and he

near the end of the game Chooky needs one ball with three balls left blue pink and black. You have seen it all running away all your luck running away out the pockets you were on top for a time Josie stopped at your table on his way to have a piss from the big pin school just as you long-potted a good black in the top left-hand pocket and he said bonny Paddy making you chalk your cue like George Raft and you were winning but it has all run away out the pockets and that's how it goes in this game and now you don't think you have it in you to win the nerves are getting the better of you you don't think you have the guts it takes guts to come from behind and be

play the blue slowly to the middle pocket but you are trembling inside no guts you don't hit the ball with confidence you are gritting your teeth if you lose this game you are out finished skint and so you hit it with this thought worrying you and the blue ball seems to take on this no-confidence the way it runs over the nap as if it is saying this guy knows he is not going to win and it hits the knuckle of the pocket without any will then trembles and stops hanging over the edge. All Chooky has to do is hit it anyhow for it to drop. So now you need snookers at the pink and if he pots that you need a lawyer. You play the pink not taking any chances leaving it fairly safe waiting for the chance of a snooker that

and Charlie comes in and stands by the table you tell him the grim news there is hope here you ask him to sub you a shilling and he gives it to you without even taking a breath what a pal just as Chooky pots the pink you can't win that one it's all over bar

can go again. You can swallow your saliva rev up your nerve chalk your cue and say we'll go again two shillings or clear a

shilling down and the loser plays the two sets you wonder
where you will get the money to pay for the two sets if you get
beat maybe Tam will stick you but it will be terrible asking him
what are you talking like that for even though Charlie gets you
a lend of Josie's cue who has just finished playing you have
already made up your mind to be a loser you would

all on the black ball the last ball on the table what they call a
black ball fight and your turn to play you need a ball each so
this is it whoever pots this wins and your turn to play you look
at all the faces standing round the table everybody stops to
watch a black ball fight with a bet on even the fellas on the next
tables stop to see who is going to pot the ball in the bag and
this makes you even more nervous but you hope you are not
showing it and you hit the black ball but as soon as you hit it
you see it does not believe in you any more than the blue
which beat you in the last game and your stomach is raw and
acid as you watch it making its way to the middle pocket
hitting the knuckle again trembling on the edge and dropping
in they all

you collect the bets from Chooky pay Charlie back and walk
out for your tea a shilling up well that's how it goes in
snooker.

Going past Murchie's, I collected fourpenceworth of tattie
scones that m'mother had told me to get on the way home and
went in for my tea. As I opened the door I bumped into Dan.
He tapped me on the shoulder as if to draw my attention as I
put the scones on the table. When I turned round he put his
thumbs in his braces, looked down at me and said
– *You silly groom,*
  Put down thy broom
  And let Lord Byron pass!
  Kidding on as usual. I laughed back at him.
– What was that, daddy? It's a saying isn't it?
– An oul' saying,
  You silly groom,

> *Put down thy broom*
> *And let Lord Byron pass,*

ses he, tapping the man with his cane, la-de-da, ye see ...
— Aye, and who ... where ...
— Who's this it was now, a big fella, ye know, terrible tall, he
stood about six feet I'm sure. White britches, lovely smooth
white britches, aye, it was the Empire y'see ... This play, they
were doing this play and the whole of Belfast had come out to
see it. I forget now who it was, the great O'Leary, was it the
great O'Leary? Yis,
— *And let Lord Byron pass!*

Ses this wee fella, turning round to him and him not the size
of a flea ... It was the groom, you see ... This wee fella, a
great favourite with the Belfast audiences ... Ses he,
— *You silly ass,*
> *There's room to pass*
> *Between the wall and I!*

Yis, there's room to pass between the wall and I, straight up to
him and the Belfast audience went mad, that's one up to him,
they said, and they clapped him so much he had to come over
to the edge of the stage and take a bow before going back to his
place again. And the great Lord, y'know, himself, didn't know
where to look. Yis, the wee fella says, there's room to pass
between the wall and I ... And the lord, the bigfella, y'know,
was raging, he was raging so he was. He put his monocle in,
looked the wee groom up and down and marched off the stage
... And the people booed him off the stage ... Yis, they farted
at him and booed him off the stage, so they did ...

The oldfella was in a great mood, his Saturday night mood.
And then Annie came in and when we turned to look at her
the corners of her mouth were down to her chin. Something
must be up with her, you could always tell by looking to see
which way her mouth was set and how clear her ferntickles
were. Maggie turned from the hob after putting down a pan of
fried tattie scones and, seeing Annie, said
— Come in hen and get your tea. What's the matter then, hen?
Have they been saying something to you, have they been
saying something to you in the street?

–No, it's not that, mammy. It was all right in the street. It was Missus Morgan was telling me ... D'y'know what she was just this minute telling me?

–No.

–You know wee Tommy Wilson, don't you? Wee Tommy Wilson ...

–And I'm sure I do. Wasn't Patrick with him a wee while since round at oul' McKellar's sale.

And I put in,

–I'll never forget that day.

Annie went on,

–Well, Missus Morgan was just telling me ... he's died in the Sanatorium. Is that not terrible?

M'mother said

–Oh, Cripes, Hammet, Mijowell, is that what you're telling me? Oh, is that not a blessed shame, is that not a shame.

–It was galloping consumption so it was, Missus Morgan said.

–Galloping consumption, oh jay, tt-tt-tt!

Dan scratched the back of his head and said

–The poor wee fella. I knew his face. He was a brave and cheery wee fella so he was and he must have been quare and sick all the time.

I looked back to that day and thought it was funny that he would not be anywhere in the town any more or at the Unemployed School. Where was he?

I remembered the heat and his drawn face and that terrible cough and the last words he said to me – *Ah, well, we'd better come on if m'mother is to get us fish suppers this night.*

16

The next day being Sunday, in the afternoon I wandered into
the street, not much thinking of where I was going and not
having any plans. The street was quiet, a lot of people were
away out with their families, it being a good day, and there
were not more than two leaning out of the windows and the
truce was still being recognised by Jeannie Aitken's supporters.
I sat down on the wall of the Church of the Nazarene and
looked up to Princes Street at the people going up and down and
trying to spot the make of any motor that would be going past.

Yaller Kennedy came over and sat beside me on the wall. He
pulled something out of his pocket and put his hand over it,
hiding it from me.
- Did you ever see the man that died with a hardon?
- Eh?
- The man that died with a hardon.
  My face got red.
- Ach, I've seen that all right.
- No, you haven't.
- How do you know?
- You haven't seen this.
- What are you talking about?
- The man that died with a hardon. Look.
  He uncovered his hand and there was a matchbox lying on
his outstretched palm. He pulled it open slowly. Inside was the
carved wooden figure of a man lying flat on his back. The lid
of the matchbox was slowly uncovering him, his chest then his
stomach. When the pit of his stomach came into view and the
tops of his thighs, suddenly from between his legs up sprung a
piece of bicycle valve tubing with the red head of a match
stuck in the top and stood up straight.
- Y'see. The man that died with a hardon. I made it with my
pen-knife.
  It set me thinking about the lassies again and *True Confessions* and Jean Harlow. He said
- Have you got it yet?

–Eh … Well … You'd only be jealous if I told you.

–Jimmy Brady got it on Wednesday night.

–Did he. Who from?

–Mary Morrison.

–She's a snecker.

–Jimmy and Alec Morgan took her and Susan Gillespie over the Bath Rocks and Jimmy got it.

–How d'ye know? I bet he only said it.

–We went bushing. A crowd of us went bushing and we saw them. Jimmy got a ride. He had her clothes up.

–I bet you didn't. You're only codding.

–If you don't believe me, come with me now. I'm going bushing out the Plantation. Will you not come along with me?

–Aye, all right.

He was making me feel all fruity and hot flannels again.

–Wait till I get my spying glasses.

He went into the house and was away for a while before he came climbing furtively out of his side window carrying an old pair of spying glasses.

–You've got all modern equipment. Where did you get them?

–They're the oldfella's. He had them in the Great War.

At the Plantation we sat down on a partly hidden hillock to survey the field.

–You have to wait till you see a couple. Then when you see them going into the bushes you can creep up. You've got to not make a sound, mind you. Sometimes the fella runs after you. Wee Willie Tomelty got a black eye the other night.

He scanned all round with the glasses. Then he put them down.

–There's nothing yet. D'you want to see a dirty picture?

I wish I could stop my face getting red.

–You bet.

He drew a postcard from his pocket and showed it to me. It was a woman on a high stool turned half sideways on. She was bare naked but the best parts of her were covered with what looked like a table-cloth. But her tits looked to be bare only you had to screw up your eyes to see them for they were in a kind of shadow. You could just see her ju-jubes on the ends if you looked long enough so that wasn't bad even though the postcard was cracked in about a hundred places and covered in jam and pocket fluff and the remains of a spearmint caramel.

– Boys. That's hot stuff. Where did you get that?

– I gave three Woodbines for it.

– That's all right. It's worth it. I wouldn't mind one myself. Could you get one for me?

– I'll see. Would you give four Woodbines?

– Four. I thought you said three.

– Aye. But three and one for me. That's four.

– All right. Yes.

He began to scan the horizon again and stopped at a point about north by north-west.

– Here. There's two now. Walking along.

– Where?

– Over there by the burn.

– Give me a look out your glasses.

He handed them to me. They weighed about a ton. I looked through them at the couple. I saw she was wearing a blue serge costume jacket and skirt but didn't get time to look at the fella before Yaller bagged them off me again. Anyway, I could see the couple plain enough without them. Suddenly, they dodged into some whin bushes. Yaller took the glasses away from his eyes and turned to me in a pant.

– C'mon, we're after them.

Keeping out of sight as much as possible, we made our way down to the burn, crossed by jumping from stone to stone where there were some big ones so as not to make a noise on the wooden bridge. When we drew near to the bushes, Yaller halted and said in an undertone,

– Stop here awhile and give them time to get started.

We sat down for a while well out of sight while Yaller hummed and hawed and bit his nails. After he had got himself into a right lather, he turned to me, put his fingers up to his lips and signed to follow him. We crawled along behind a hedge until we reached the bushes. Yaller had slung the spying-glasses on his back by the strap. Saying nothing, he turned to me, pointed ahead and began to edge forward towards the bushes on his elbows and knees like a Red Indian, keeping well down in the long grass. I followed doing the same and after some time found myself in among the whins in a spot by myself. Yaller would be tracking from another angle.

I was scared to breathe now in among the green darkness of the whins and I could hear my heart thumping. Very, very slowly and carefully I crawled forward peering through the bushes trying to see signs of the quarry. A flash of white caught my eye. I held my breath and eased myself towards it, trying to see through the gorse. The white seemed to be moving, framed in a small gap in the whins. As close now as I dared to go, I put my hand forward and slowly pulled down a branch. I looked through. A girl's leg with a silk stocking on it. I craned further. Her knee. Her thigh. Fancy garters where the stockings ended. Bare thighs. Skirt being pulled up while her legs thrashed about. Skirt right up now. A pair of artificial silk knickers. Bulging because there was a hand inside them groping about. Little squeals as she tried to stop the fella who kept shushing her. I craned forward as far as I could go and made another gap in the branches.

I was looking at a face in which a pair of eyes were staring back at mine. We looked at each other, hypnotised, for what seemed a long time. It was Jeannie Aitken's cousin from Stevenston, Puddin' Dodds, one of the hardest nuts in the Boglemart.

I didn't stop to find out if he recognised me as suddenly he lept to his feet and there was a thrashing of stockinged legs and trousers – I was away like a hare but I could hear what sounded like an elephant behind me crashing straight through the whins without stopping to go round them.

Spurting away across the open ground of the Plantation, I could hear him running behind me. Out of the gate and down the crescent I turned into South Beach Road and headed across the green. He was gaining on me. I could hear the sound of his running feet getting closer and closer. Soon I heard the thumping of his boots on the ground right behind me. I hadn't the nerve or the puff to look round. It seemed to me now that he was breathing down the back of my neck, I heard the panting of his breath coming in great gulps. Another inch and he could take the pins from me with one kick. I heard his voice.

—I'll ... I'll ... f-fughin *burst* you when I catch you. I'll, I'll fughin *burst* you!

The fear of God went right through me from my soul to my heels, acting on me like syrup of figs, my feet, including the bad one, hardly seemed to touch the ground as I took off like Sir Malcolm Campbell's Bluebird and fairly zoomed home leaving Puddin' Dodds somewhere between the South Beach and the Town Station and didn't stop till I got up the close and in the door.

It was that word *burst* that did it. No one had said that to me yet.

17

Then war broke out again.

Jeannie Aitken came home with her baby and straight-away announced that our John was the father and seven and six he would have to pay for telling the tale to her.

Harbour Place prepared for action again. All the windows went up. The expert gossips sharpened their tongues. Snipers occupied strategic positions. Coming home now meant running the gauntlet from the Church of the Nazarene to the close. It was no good trying the other end of the street. That was enemy-occupied territory. Coming that way you would have to be very brave or drunk or Jak-Wes the Ape. In fact it would be a toss-up whether you ever reached the close.

After a week of this outside and accusations and denials inside, m'mother laid down the law to John. He would have to go before the priest.

The night they went I returned to the house by the back way over the railway and Morgan's wall. When I opened the door I found the oldfella there and Annie in for a break from her work in the hotel. Dressed in her waitress's uniform, her eyes were red from crying. He had a towel in his hand.

– Come on now hen. Give your face a wipe with this towel and take your cup of tea. What were they saying to you?

– They were shouting things at me. They were saying *When's your brother going to pay for his wean*. And Jeannie Aitken came right up to me carrying the baby in a shawl and said to it *There's your auntie, look, there's your auntie*. And *Where is he the night? Where's the father tonight?* A lot of them shouted out the window again, *Send out the father of Jeannie's bairn!*

– Ah, never mind them, never mind them. They're only trying to cause trouble. They're only a lot of oul' ra-ha's, anyway, a lot of oul' ra-ha's. Come on hen and I'll take you round the corner.

He began putting on his jacket while Annie finished her tea.

– They won't say anything to you while I'm there. Better put some coal on the fire, Patrick, and empty the black pail before your mother comes in.

They left together. I went into the coalhouse to get some coal and put it on the fire. I stood looking at the flames shooting up as the coal dust ignited. I wondered how John was getting on, stuck out in the chapel with the priest among all the saints and incense. They were bringing hell fire against him. Trapped. But he would outwit them. He would find a way. I sang the song under my breath hoping he would receive the message.

– *Camerad – o*,

I went into the coalhouse again and got the slop pail. It was full nearly to overflowing with old twisted and rolled-up papers floating on top of the slops. Balancing it to avoid spilling, I made my way slowly down the stairs and out to the back yard.

Cleaning the pail out at the spicket after emptying it, I heard familiar footsteps, looked round and saw m'mother and John arriving back. They were going up the stairs, not speaking a word and she was keeping about six yards between herself and John. When I opened the door, he was standing by the window looking out and m'mother had just finished hanging up her coat. She walked over to the fire, sat on a chair and rested her head on her hand. Nobody spoke. I put the pail back in the coalhouse and tried to make myself invisible. I might well have been for all the attention that was paid to me.

The oldfella came in. He looked from one to the other from under his eyebrows before speaking.

– Aye, you're there. You've come back. There's a wee cup of tea in the pot if you want it.

– No. I want no cups of tea. I'll drink no more cups of tea. It's a cup of poison we may as well all be drinking.

– Did you see Father Reilly?

– Aye, see him. Did I see him? Yes, I saw him all right. And the playboy here. Aye, the truth came out of him. We may as well all pack our traps, as the saying is, and go away as far again. Sure, we'll never be settled. There's no resting place in this world for us.

– Did ... Did the worst come to the worst?

– Oh, did it not? Yes, the worst came to the worst all right. Ask your big son over there. Your son that's driven us all into disgrace. Oh, it came out of him all right.

She turned to John and spoke to him directly,

– Come over you here from that window when I'm speaking to you. There's no good in hiding your face out of the window.

John left the window reluctantly and moved to the middle of the floor where he hovered around the table. I was sitting over by the coalhouse beside the wash-stand. M'mother pointed the finger of scorn at John.

– There he is. The playboy himself!

Dan said

– What'll we do now ...

– Yes, Father Reilly got it out of him. He wouldn't dare tell a lie to the priest the way he was telling lies to his mother. And, as they say, it is seven and six a week he will have to pay now right enough, I'm thinking. What do you think of that?

– Seven and sixpence a week out of the few shillings he gets. We won't be able to live at all.

– But I wouldn't mind the money. It's not the money I'm thinking about. It's the disgrace to our good name. And the dirt. The dirty thing he's done. Sinning his soul with a dirty sin of impurity. Things that you couldn't even speak about...

She got up from the chair and stood in front of John to get a better shouting position.

– ... And him brought up cleanly to be a good-living boy like all his family were before him. The dirty scut!

She drew off and slapped him hard across the right side of his face.

– Now! That's what you are!

She slapped him across the left side of his face with the other hand.

– That you would treat your mother like dirt after all that's been done for you. Take that you dirty scoundrel! You reptile, ye!

Inflamed, she began to rain punches and slaps all over John's face, driving him back to the wall. He took them with his head up, not dodging any of them, making no sound or any attempt to ward off the blows.

– You have disgraced our name and disgraced our whole family and my dear mother, God rest her, will be turning in her grave! There's a curse! There's someone will put their curse on ye, so they will!

All this time she was laying into him as if he was a punching bag. She now lifted a plate from the table and smashed it over his head. It split the skin on his forehead over his eye. But he continued to stand with his head up, saying nothing, his face wooden and the blood beginning to run down it. I ran over and began plucking at m'mother's skirt from behind.

– Don't hit him any more, mammy, don't hit him any more!

The old man rushed between m'mother and John with his hands up like a referee in Madison Square Garden. Maggie shrieked

– The curse o' God on ye!

Part 3 Jak-Wes the ape escapes again!

18

Mister Toner looked over his glasses at us and, his eyes shining, announced
– Boys, I am happy to tell you that the entire Unemployed School will become employed as from Wednesday. The *S.S. Lord Dalwhinnie* which is lying in the old dock needs ... eh ...

He looked at a paper in his hand.
– ... eh ... needs chipping, red-leading and her bilges cleaned out. The Labour Bureau in co-operation with the boiler scaling company have agreed that the job should be done by the School for Unemployed Youths. You will all get the rest of the day off ...

A big cheer from us.
– ... But I want you to line up and march round to the Labour Bureau with me now where your name and particulars will be taken down. You've to get thirty-seven and sixpence a week pay, your cards stamped and there's nearly two weeks work. On Wednesday morning you will report to the First Mate of the *Lord Dalwhinnie* at half-past-seven. As you will be away early today, I hope you will all go straight home and not hang about and get into trouble.

After another cheer we lined up, quietly enough for us, and marched down the Inches Road to the Burroo, getting raspberries and chyacks from the gamblers behind the flute band hut, the betting men at Mick Kelly's and a gang working on the railway track.

Coming out of the Burroo, I had a look at the Brag school in Moon McMillan's wash-house but, seeing that it was wasting away for lack of iron, I made my way homewards to see if I could bum a cup of tea.

Going round the other way this time, past the Clydesdale Bank and E. Currie's corner for the chance of picking up a decent-sized fag-end – without any luck – I turned into Harbour Place at the Nicol's Bar side, right into the centre of a gang of kids who, seeing me, joined hands and danced around me singing

– *His brother bairned the lassie-o,*
The lassie-o,
The lassie-o,
His brother bairned the lassie-o
Around about Mary mah tansie,

giving me an odd kick with their tackety boots as they went past. Says I,

– Away owa that wi' ye!

and walked on, not bothering my head. Before I had taken three steps, the contents of a slop bucket landed on the pavement two inches before my feet, missing me but splashing my flannels and leaving them decorated with tea leaves so that I looked like one of Troise's Gypsy Mandoliers. A window shut quickly above me. Jeannie Aitken had relatives at the end of the street. While looking up I nearly pitched forward flat on my face, having tripped over a leg which someone sitting on a doorstep had accidentally stuck out in front of me. Why did I come down this way?

A bit further down I found myself in the middle of a bunch of Herald Street hoppers which closed tight when I reached the centre where I found myself being batted about from one to the other like a tennis ball. After I escaped from that lot, an old biddy suddenly flew out of the big pen, her shawl billowing in the wind and, baring her stumpy gums, screeched at me,

– Awa', y' durty wee whelp!

– Och, away and mind your hens.

In the attic, John was the only one home. He sat gazing out the window, a bit drawn looking, but still keeping the twinkle in his eye which he always had no matter what.

– How's Jak-Wes the Ape?

– Camer-ad-o! All right, pal.

– Were you finished early with the motor?

– Yep.

– Captain Cobb at Daytona Beach.

– We broke the record again, ha-ha.

– Aye, you beat Tommy MacNamara's horse home along the shore.

– *And we killed a hare*
  And a hen or two

– *And a pig-arrah-passing by*

– *And we're off on a hibbity,*
  hibbity, hibbity,
  Hi-hi-hi!

We had a laugh at this.

– John ... Mind you used to tell me a story about our ranch in the Rocky Mountains where there was a horse all ready for me called Silver King?

– It had a harness shining with silver and a Spanish saddle...

– And I was to have two pearl-handled guns...

– And they would call you the Celtic Kid.

– Aye ... It was a story, I know ... but...

– Maybe it will come true.

– You've never been to the Rocky Mountains yet, have you?

– No, but I might be going some day ... And I might get a ranch.

– You never know.

– Do you still want a horse? I'll have a horse for you.

– What, the coalman's horse?

– No, the bucket-cart horse, ha-ha.

–*What do you feed your horse on?*

–*Coal!*

–Ha-ha-ha. Tom Sanstichi. D'ye know Tom Sanstichi in the pictures? That's who you look like.

–The Sea Wolf.

–*And the muscles of his brawny arms*
  Stood out like iron bands.

–Look at that.

He rolled up his shirt sleeve and flexed his muscle and it had grown bigger than ever. I said to him,

–Do you think my muscles might get like that?

–You should keep lifting heavy things. Practise lifting weights.

–D'y'think you could still lift me up with your teeth?

–You're getting a bit too big for that now. Try anyway. I'll try anyway. Here ... Across the table.

I took off my jacket and lay across the table, face down. He came over and bent down. He said

–Look, my hands are behind my back.

I looked round and saw that he had his hands clasped behind him. My trouser braces began to tighten when he had them in his teeth then, very slowly, I began to rise from the table. It was a funny feeling to rise like that and just hang suspended like from a crane. I tried to keep myself as still as possible and not shuggle about in case he hurt his mouth. I rose about three inches off the table then slowly he let me down again. I jumped up and put my jacket on saying

–That's great, you can still do it. I didn't think you'd be able to do it now.

–Well, you're light-boned. And you're not all that big for your age.

He made the muscles of his jaw stand out saying

–What a jaw!

–Good old Jak-Wes the Ape!

We were having a good laugh then first the oldfella came in and then m'mother and the atmosphere became all thrawing again, lightened a bit by my telling her I was getting some work.

19

Mister Toner's Burroo School Navy assembled on the deck of the *S.S. Lord Dalwhinnie* at half-past-seven in the morning and the First Mate stood glaring at us. The ship was not in the old dock at all but lying outside at anchor. We had been brought aboard by Pilot boat. And part of our job was to help the skeleton crew left on board to take it in. There was a good stiff wind blowing from the direction of the snow-capped peaks of Arran – all right for those who had balaclavas which was everybody except us. Wearie Nicolson said
– I don't know where that wind's comin' from but I know where it's going – right up the hole in the arse of my strides.

In fact there were various holes displayed on all sides and the breeze was fairly playing about the lot of them. The Mate, well covered in a deep sea gansey under his deck coat, looked at us as if we were tadpoles and sneered.
– Any of you crowd been to sea before?

His accent was as cor blimey as the Prince of Wales'. But the replies were piped back quickly.
– I've been round the bay in McLauchlin's motor boat.
– I've been to Arran on the Glen Sannox.
– I've been on the steamboats at the fair.
– Give us a job to get us warm, mister.
– I've been on the drudger.

The Mate fixed on the last speaker and, eyeing him up and down, said
– Where did you operate and what did you sail as?
– It never left the dock and the Harbour Polis chased me off.

The Mate said something that sounded like *a bunch of Scotch rascals* and continued to cast his eye hither and yon. Placing his arms akimbo he said
– I want one of you for the chain-locker. We're going to up anchor. Any volunteers?

This was the signal for a general movement to get out of the way. The words *chain-locker* only struck a faint chord with me and I'm sure not many of the rest had much idea what it was but the way he said it sounded bad enough. Dreaming, as usual, I suddenly found that I had been left in a conspicuous position. The Mate must have been a very hard man to pick the skinniest skelf of the lot for he bawled at me,

– You – down the chain-locker and prepare to stow the anchor.

I ambled forward in a daze, not knowing whether to make for the blunt end or the sharp end until one of the regular hands took pity on me and showed me where it was, an open hatchway on the fo'c'sle head down which a ladder disappeared into the ship.

I clambered down the ladder, hung the hurricane lamp that the sailor had given me on a bolt hole and, by the light of this, found that I could see about two feet in front of my nose. In time, when my eyes became used to the blackness, I could make out the locker dimly. Well named, a locker it was certainly, about seven feet square it looked to me and covered all over, deck and bulkhead in the remains of thick black oily grease. My heart came into my mouth as I remembered what I had heard about chain-lockers before. Lurid tales about deck-hands having an arm crushed by the chain or being completely buried under the giant links.

– Before I had time to think any more there was a noise like the crashing of big guns, the locker began to shudder and the anchor chain, each link about the size of myself, slackened and, through a large slit, began to descend, link by link. There was no escaping it, I had to grab the first link and haul it into position. Then another and another to form a coil. Down they came, non-stop, and soon they were wet and slimy with sea-weed and then oozing with dirty grey oily mud. Sometimes they didn't fall the way you wanted them to and jammed then each one behind would jam as well and I had to work like a madman to catch up in order to prevent the anchor chain fouling into a fankle – a fankle that would have had to be unravelled by an acetylene burner. They came down angrily and without mercy these huge links almost impossible to grip hold of and guide into something like a coil in the semi-darkness, while I sweated drops of blood to keep the chain from fouling and at the same time, I felt sure, for my life, I was frightened stiff that if the chain jammed it might buckle out and crush me against the bulkhead.

Out of the corner of my eye – which was all I could spare – I saw someone climbing down the ladder. When he got within range I could make out that it was a young cadet and he set about straightaway to help me but I couldn't even spare a sideways glance of thanks as we both toiled away grimly and without stop, not a sound or a word except heavy grunts and pechs and a yell every time we jammed a finger in the links, the cries all but blotted out anyway by the crashing jang of the chain. They stopped heaving for a short time, just long enough for us to think we were going to have time to get our breaths back, then on again before we had time to draw them.

It was a bone-jarring nightmare and when it was all over we both lay against the bulkhead all out and peching for breath in the small amounts of air that was in that space, the foul smell of the oily mud nearly choking us, our hands bleeding and covered from head to foot in muck and grease.

Bye and bye, we staggered up on deck. The Mate approached us with a sly grin on his mug, saying
– You're good lads and you'll make good sailors.

What, in the Burroo School Navy? Some joke. I could see what it was. We were going to do the work of full-blown highly paid ship's riggers and some pockets were going to be lined and a lot of palms greased around the town. The old cheap labour racket again.

Knowing that the only way we could back out would be to swim for it and it was too deep and too far even for Spud Murphy, they got us, along with the skeleton crew, to handle the ship into drydock – a job for pros if there ever was one – in the course of which, Tommy McWilliams from Kilwinning who was used more to howking tatties than handling a ship, dropped his two middle fingers to the bottom of the drydock, these having been cut off between a wire hawser and the scuppers when he tried to lift a stanchion by putting his hand under the hawser and heaving.

So that was the score at the end of that day – one knocked right out and the rest of us only crippled, a good seven and sixpence – a day's pay – worth of our blood, sweat and skin left behind on the good ship *S.S. Lord Dalwhinnie*, that dirty stinking old tramp and its dirty stinking old Mate.

Most of the night spent by me scraping the muck off my body and by m'mother scraping the muck off my togs. She has to patch a pair of the old man's strides and an old shirt for me to wear the morrow – where's the gain?

Well, now the old tub was sitting still anyway and not moving, tied up and shored up in the drydock and no more handling of her to be done. A few braves were missing when we turned to again, mostly from across the Rockies in Misk territory. The sight of water for the first time had given them a shock and sent them to the doctor for a line.

A crowd of us were sent down the holds to clean out the bilges and after that to chip and scrape the sides. There were loose ropes tied and suspended from the hatchway and we found that we could swing on these from one side of the hold to the other, sometimes alighting on the propeller shaft. So it was the jungle for a while with Spud Murphy as Tarzan. Murphy bet us he could shin up one of the ropes from the propeller shaft to the top of the hatchway and collected one and ninepence in bets after he had done it. He then bet that none of us could do it and collected another one and ninepence when none of us did. This bout of derring-do brought the second casualty when Alec Reid slipped down the rope, fell and split his skull on the propeller shaft casing. That was him away down the gangway on a stretcher and two up to the helot monsters.

The third came that week when we were put to red-leading the hold after it was chipped and scraped. To put it on the sides seemed a waste and soon we formed into gangs for a good red-lead paint fight, making the entire hold our battleground and using the ropes to swing across, slosh the paint and swing back again. We put Wee Gribbon to spreading the paint that fell on the deck with a brush and, that way, got the deck done before the sides, nothing was being wasted. For a while it looked like the Red Hell of Pitzu Palu or something as we swung about on the ropes from side to side, filling the air with red rain. Two, who had crashed into each other in the centre, now fought a duel with their brushes while hanging from the rope with one hand. But who's this? Swinging through the air with the greatest of ease, faster and fleeter than any of the red devils, hanging on with one hand, a full pot of red lead in the other? No one but Bloody Red Baron Murphy. At the end of his swing, the pot was up-ended and the paint went flying through the air at the enemy. I got some of it but Wee Gribbon took the most of it and became a red man from his head to his boot soles. So, nearly blinded, he was carted off to have his eyes cleaned out. I had red hair for the next three months.

At the height of the shemozzle the bo'sun had come and gone, everybody too busy to take any notice of him and, having no luck in trying to save his paint, fetched the Mate. He took one look and sent for the Harbour Polis.

Even so, we held the hold and nobody dare come down the ladder after the first harbour dud got a pair of red trousers to go with his natty blue uniform for trying. This sortie was again brought off by Murphy who, seeing the uniformed legs come into view, flashed across on his rope and changed the Dick's colour scheme before he could get to the top of the ladder again. The shouts of the Burroo School Navy echoed through the hold in triumph.

We only came up when our ammunition ran out and our stomachs told us it must be getting near going-home time anyway.

The bulk of the red lead was on us but we had left some below mostly in the form of slogans painted on the sides of the hold such as *The Mate is a Cornish pastie-faced bastard. Up Winton Rovers. Up yu. Geordies go home yacunts. Spud was here. Kee-Kee Tam. The Mate's a poof. I beefed the Mate signed the Beefer.*

They lined us up on the deck and the Mate, who was in full

command of the ship because the skipper was on leave, marched up and down in front of us with his hands behind his back as if it was the mutiny on the *Bounty*.

– Turning my ship into a shebeen ... Causing a rough-house. They told me you were all savage here—
– Away back to Geordieland!
– Who said that?
– No' me.
– No' me.
– No' me.
– ... You are all getting good money—
– Starvation wages!
– Yer bunks are full o' bugs!
– And you're full o' shite!
– Who said that? I could have you all keel-hauled!
– What! Did nobody tell ye we were in the drydock?
– Ha-ha-ha!
– ... not overworked ... and behave yourselves like—
– What about Tommy McWilliams' two fingers?
– Aye, that's right.
– He'll not even get compen'.
– Your shipping company is a bunch of thievin' fughin gits!
– That'll be enough of that talk.
– O-oh, listen to Jessie!
– Do you want some cold cream?
– No, he likes Navy cake the best.
– Ha-ha-ha!

The Mate, his face by then the only white part of the ship, had us all put ashore for the rest of the day and we all got docked half-a-day's wages.

20

That night I met John secretly on the rocks down the steps from the Barony Church.

– Have you got them?

– They're in my inside pocket. Come on Squareshoulders.

– Okay, Jak-Wes the Ape.

The tide was out to its fullest, the sun going down over the harbour and the shore stretched in front of us away into the distance to the other side of the bay and the red roof of the Beach Pavilion which we were headed for to see the stage variety show. *This week – Lodgers and Codgers! Featuring the Clyde's own favourite – Sammy Murray! Direct from the Metropole Glasgow!*

– Where d'ye get them?

– Jimmy Stewart got six from Harry Kemp for a tip and he gave me three. I gave one to Finn Donnelly and kept two for us.

He drew from his pocket the two blue cards that got you into the Beach Pavilion for half price. That meant threepence each in the back seats. He had passed a secret message to me at supper time, not being allowed to yarn with me as he had disgraced the family. I was changed into my grey flannels and a white open-necked shirt with one of John's old blue serge jackets that he had grown out of but I still had red lead rings round my eyes and my hair rivalled Annie's ginger when it shone in the rays of the setting sun. John's jacket was so shiny you could nearly see your face in it but over his working shirt he had on a stiff clean white collar – the kind you could buy in Woolworths – with long peaks and a pinhead knot in his tie. He always went in for knots so wee you could hardly see them – very gallus.

Left behind us the screeking and screeching of Harbour Place, the smoke rising from the chimbleys and, beyond Christie's Yard, the masts of the *S.S. Lord Dalwhinnie* swift panging my stomach and as swiftly forgotten in the rising excitement of the evening ahead.

Nearing the end of the rocks, the air was filled with salt, strong and heavy from the clean waters of the Firth, the tang adding spring to our step as we started off across the still-wet sandy strand to the red roofs of the dream castle in the distance.

—Are you driving yet, John?

—I drove it today for a bit. I take it in and out the garage. He's to let me take it along the shore road for a bit the morrow.

—Is he? Is it a Morris?

—It's a Morris Cowley. If you can get round to the garage sometime when I'm taking it out, I might give you a hurl.

—I bet you I could drive it. I'll try and get round ... Jak-Wes ... Here, John ... Did Jak-Wes die right enough in the story or was he only letting on?

—Maybe he was only letting on.

—Maybe he'll return. *The Return of Jak-Wes the Ape*. You could make it another story.

—Aye. The return of Jak-Wes the Ape.

—By Zane O'Connor.

—Ha-ha. Or H. De Vere O'Connor.

—That's a good one. Where was it he was supposed to die. It was in the mountains, wasn't it? In the story, I mean.

—Yes. The Mountains of the Moon. In Africa.

—After he had saved the garrison.

—Aye. The Foreign Legion.

—They were at their last gasp.

—Yes. And then Jak-Wes appears. Across the desert.

—*Till the Sands of the Desert Grow Co-old*.

—Ha-ha.

—Then he saved the garrison. The leader was that one like Gary Cooper.

—Yes. Or Victor McLaglen in *The Lost Patrol*.

—It wasn't Victor, John. Everybody thinks it was Victor. It was his brother, Cyril.

—Was it?

—Aye, Cyril McLaglen.

—Well. Cyril or Victor. But Jak-Wes saves him, anyway, Patrick.

102

–And becomes his comrade for life. But he's wounded.
–The Arabs chase him across the desert. Bleeding from his wound, he escapes to the Mountains of the Moon.
–And that's when the hero hears his last song coming over the desert, isn't it?
–Yes, Patrick. He hears far away the last song of Jak-Wes. He had once befriended Jak-Wes and saved him from some hunters who were out to kill him.
–And he came back to pay his debt.
–The song comes over the desert faintly, *Camerad* ... and the last note trails away ... *O-o-o!*
–It's a great story. You should write it down.
–Maybe I will.
–Maybe Jak-Wes the Ape will come back again.
–Well, you never know, Patrick.
–Maybe *you're* Jak-Wes.
–You never know that, eithers.

He swung his arms by his sides, growled and came after me. I ran like mad and he chased me for a long way along the sands, right across the Galloway Burn. Now, we found that the Beach Pavilion had become larger while we were talking and then we saw the lights being switched on suddenly so we trotted the rest of the way on the firm sand between the very wet and the very dry and soon we were there, coming out from the dusk and up the steps into the bright lights.

A piece of paper free with all the acts on it. The lights go out. *Trixie Dodd and her Piano Accordion.* Full highland dress but her kilt very short showing a lace petticoat. Try to see up her clothes. I wonder if John is doing the same beside me. A Scottish selection. Build up to the overture *Light Cavalry.* Big number. A good clap. As she swings round to go off for the last time a flash of white knickers. More clapping. Hullaw! Curtain. *Wearie and Wullie, Scotia's favourites.* Wullie dressed up as a woman. E-e-e-eh! Screeches of ecstasy from the old biddies beside us at the back. Here's my pay. What's this? Short time. Smack. You've come to the wrong place – *Screech!* – Blackout. Hullo, dearie. Hullo. Is this the place?

You're telling me. Screech from the biddies as the balloons up his jersey slip down. I was told to knock three times and ask for Nellie Duff. That's right dear, I'm Nellie Duff. You look more like Plum Duff to me. Ha-ha-ha! You're that fresh, what do you want? I'm fairly ready for it. You look it. Ha-ha-ha! I've been at sea for three months. You look as if you've been in Barlinnie for six months. Ha-ha-ha! I can't wait, let me get at it. *Screech!* How would you like it? On a plate, if you don't mind. A plate, are you trying to be funny? What's this, then? This is the best kip shop in the town. A kip shop? I thought they said it was a *chip* shop. Ha-ha-ha! Curtain. Clapping. Encore. Curtain.

Alistair Lennox. Scotia's bard. Direct from special engagement at the Parish Hall, Cowdenbeath!

Looks as if he is wearing Trixie Dodd's kilt, it's half-way up his bum. Kiltie caul bum. Some of us at the back begin to chant

—Kiltie, kiltie, caul bum!

Alistair with one hand in the air. He doesn't come in at the end of the introduction. Chanting. *Kiltie, kiltie, caul bum!*

Hector Donald, the manager, rushing out from the wings. Now, please, let us hear this lovely song. Give the singer a chance. Quiet. Piano again.

Alistair. There is a morn in flowery May, and sweetest night in autumn mild ... e'en there her other works are foiled by the Bonny Lass o' Ballochmyle. Ae fond kiss and then we sever. Ae fareweel and then forever deep in heart-wrung tears I'll pledge thee, warring sighs and groans I'll wage thee. Hullaw! Hullaw! Encore! He's good, isn't he? He's got a great voice, kiltie caul bum or not. Encore! ... though this was fair and that was bra' and yon the toast o' a' the toon, I sighed and said amang them a', ye are na' Mary Morrison. Hullaw! Good old Alistair! Curtain. Lights dim and come up again. Drums.

And now. What you have all been waiting for. The Clyde coast favourite. The one and only Sammy Murray!! Hullaw! Good old Sammy! Here he is! Hullaw!

Here! I like this place. Hullo. Aye, hullo. Aye, that wee wumman in the third row kens me. Is that not right, hen? Is that not right? – *Screech!* – No, that other one beside her. Stand up, hen. Yes, I saw you. I was in for a sly drink in the Windy Ha' and here she was doing the same thing – *Screech!* – Five minutes away from her man, she says. I hope he's not here tonight, hen. Oh, he is? – Ha-ha-ha! – Where is he? Oh, there he is. Right beside her. Can we have the spotlight over here? Aye, the spotlight over here. There he is. Stand up, mister – Hullaw! Ha-ha-ha – I hope you don't mind but I walked her home, afterwards – *Screech!* – After we had a wee hauf each, that is. What, you didn't know she took drink? Oh well, I've got news for you. She would drink you out of hoose and hame. – Ha-ha-ha! – Oh no, well I'm only gegging, you know? I walked her hame because she was frightened of the dark. She says the bogles might get me. She says I'm not going down Quay Street in the dark by myself. And no wonder. I went down by myself in the daylight and I was tapped for a shilling three times, lost sixteen shillings at pontoons and reached the other end without my trousers! – *Screech!* – No wonder she was frightened. There're some places round here, I'm tellin' ye. Clare tae Goad! Take my lodgings, for instance. The landlady's got a face like a fiddle and she's always on it. Whit? She charges you a penny to tell you the time. Mind you, she's very economical. The same notice is up all over the house. The same one. Just one word. *Don't!* – Ha-ha-ha! – We're all pilgrims, she says. Pilgrims of the night. Yes, pilgrims of the night. Yes. I met them the first night I was there. I didn't have to join them. They came to me. And so I just sang a song, the song I always sing, and it goes like this,

Turning down the be-e-edclothes,
Oh, what a sight!
Jumping about in their thous-ands,
The pilgrims of the night!

Ha-ha-ha! Ha-ha-ha! Hullaw! Good old Sammy! Encore! 'Core! Bows. Curtain. House lights up. *Interval.*

John from his pocket a penny poke of monkey nuts. Munch. Happy. Share. Munch all the interval. The house lights dim. Hector Donald, the manager, enters before the curtain. Plus-fours, bow-tie, American specs. A paper in his hand. Good old

Hector! Hullaw! Go on Hector, yourself! He puts his hand up for silence.

Well ladies and gentlemen I hope you are all enjoying the show tonight which we spared no expense to present to you and we always try to bring you the best talent on the coast I think you will all agree that it is a very good bill tonight with everybody's favourite the great Sammy Murray not forgetting the very talented supporting bill some of them already going places in show business Alistair Lennox has got a wireless audition next week I'm sure you will be pleased to hear and Trixie Dodd is to represent Motherwell next Sunday in the Lanarkshire finals of the Hohnerr Piano Accordion Trophy next week we have a very good bill for you with exceptional attractions which our talent scouts have been busy getting together for you from all corners of Scotia's braes this spectacular show is called Caledonian Capers with some great new acts including the death-defying leap for life through a ring of daggers and flames a Highland Panorama with the Auchenshuggle Bonnie Girl Dancers and a real waterfall on the stage the noted button-key girl accordionist Volupti your favourite soubrette Bonnie Dundee other great acts which I haven't got time to mention and retained for a second great week by enormous public demand the one and only Sammy Murray the winning number tonight is nine four six three anybody with nine four six three call at the box office on the way out for their prize thank you for your attention yours truly Hector Donald.

Good old Hector! The lights go down. *Duncan Macintosh – baritone.* An uncanny resemblance to *Wullie* of the *Wearie and Wullie* double act.
– *Till the sands of the desert*
  Grow co-old.
Dressed in the uniform of the French Foreign Legion. Painted palm trees behind him.
– *And the stones of the pass*
  Turn to go-old . . .
Mind wandering. Think again of Jak-Wes the Ape fleeing across the desert with the blood from his wound making a trail

on the sand. Did he die? Will he return? The desert gives way to stony ground and now the mountains begin, the Mountains of the Moon where it is very cold at night – do apes feel the cold through their fur? – and snakes lurk behind the boulders and the moon itself shines in the clear cold desert sky...

– *Forever I'll be true*
Till the sands of the desert
Gro-oo-ow cold!

Hullaw! Encore! Drums. The piano. A spotlight. Hullaw! Good old Sammy!

And here I am, did you think I was not coming back? Big Aggie's Man. That's me. Yes, here I am again. Is this where the nobs hang out? – *Screech!* – Oh, hello, hen. There y'are. I hope I didn't keep you waiting...

... Mind wandering again supposing that was me up there, what would I do? Pushed out on to the stage by Hector Donald. Try to get in for nothing, would you? Go on, out on that stage and work it off. Well, I could always say *Boys how I envied McGinty*, I would be a great tear altogether, a great tare as m'daddy says but he knows *The Shooting of Dan McGrew*, I wish I knew that one and the immortal Wullie can say *The Face on the Bar-room Floor* all the way through to the end when he's in Nicol's Bar and everybody stops to listen, all the dockers and shipyard workers. They say you would see a tear in a hard man's eye some night, it has been known, when Wee Johnny Hunter sings *White Wings they Never Grow Wearie*. I've only got McGinty but if I got my nerve up I would imitate Lionel Barrymore and Eddie Cantor and they would encore me and clap and a new star would be born and Hector Donald would get me to sign a contract and it would be in *The Ardrossan and Saltcoats Herald* about the local boy who made good...

– *...Oh, I married me a lass*
The name o' Aggie,
The terror of the town of Strathnavan.
And when I go out all the people shout
There he goes, there he goes,
The piano goes dum-dum-dum-dum.

Hullaw! Good old Sammy!

Then the hall lights go on and we all stand up and the piano plays God Save The King.

A shyness welling. My feet scuffle. Unable to look at John. The monkey nuts and caramel papers scuffed as we move out. The hard bare wood of the cheap back seats. The curtain down. A world where. The shiny blue of John's jacket. Good old Jak-Wes. The way his boots are always polished. John. A penny now and again when he has it. We move out. The banging of the seats behind us all over the hall. Glare lights in the entrance you cannot see outside through the dark. Past the wee wooden ticket box office.

And out into the shawl of the dark two camerados are we sharing our own penny wonder and adventures awaiting us away across the shore the twinkling lights of home down among the dead men we must go but home home safe again you are a wee boy again Silver King knows his own way I can let the reins hang loose I canter alongside the big guy who sits straight in the saddle his jaw firm and at the end of the trail in Eldorado we'll get some tea and maybe we can make some toast at the bars of the fire.

21

In the morning shanghaied again on the slave ship but I must admit feeling a bit gallus in my working clothes, chyacking and jostling down through the harbour gates with the best of them, the shipyard workers, the dockers and the boiler scalers, shouting the odds about the Rovers' chances on Saturday against Kilwinning Rangers. And then the white skull face of the Mate, standing sneering on the deck as we troop up the gangway – enough to put you off your breakfast – waiting to nab us before we can get away to hide in the galley or the fiddley or down the fireman's fo'c'sle where you could watch them play cribbage but never be able to figure out how it was played.

The well-under-his-thumb bo'sun was standing beside him and, after making sure we had all turned to – except for Wearie Nicolson who was absent – he led us to the paint store and handed out a pot of red lead and a brush each. It was over the side this time.

Led by a couple of pro riggers we managed to get the staging around the hull in a Harry Tate's Navy kind of way and then we started red leading from the keel aloft. Not much chance of red lead fights here with eyes over the deck-rail every time you looked up and the bo'sun down on the drydock bottom watching us. Still, we managed to get in a few sloshes and just missed an A.B. – one of the Mate's toadies – with a pot of paint which dropped accidentally.

Wearie Nicolson turned up late and became the next casualty. The staging he was to share with Spud Murphy was up the hull off the drydock by the time he arrived looking half asleep as usual. The Mate sent him straight over the side down a rope-ladder and, being Wearie, he missed his foot on the staging and fell to the bottom of the drydock. A broken arm and a fractured shoulder. Lucky for him the staging was not all that high up the hull and had been due for hoisting just as he arrived. Lesson for that day – There is a special way of climbing a rope ladder which is hanging flat against the side of a ship. They didn't tell us till *after* Wearie fell. So, as there was not as much red lead flying about that day, I went home more like a speckled hen than my usual Red Indian.

The crowds jostling through the harbour gates when the five o'clock horn blew, all the feet, it sounds like an army marching, step it out, jockey for position – *straight liners, you must keep walking in straight liners* – if you tripped you would be trampled to death.

– *Bee, baw, babitee, babitee, babitee,*
 Bee, baw, babitee.
 I wouldna have a wee laddie.

I'd rather have a lassie-o, a lassie-o, a lassie-o,
I'd rather have a lassie-o,
I wouldna have a wee laddie.
Bee, baw, babitee—

went the song from a crowd of kids at Herald Street corner. But I smelt carbide in the air. And battle smoke. It hung over Harbour Place as sure as shooting, you could tell there was something up as you neared it by the different sounds in the air, the higher note of the screeching. At the corner, Nicol's Bar had just opened and the workers with a thirst were going in for their pints. There were some champion thirsts around there, the coal dust thirst, the boiler scaling thirst, the red-lead thirst and the king of them all, the iron ore thirst. The ore dockers needed about three pints before they could begin to taste the beer on their iron plated throats.

I heard somebody saying there was a fight down the street and as I turned the corner I saw a crowd scrabbling around the big pen. Then I saw Annie's red head among the crowd and I began to run.

The barging and screeching got louder as I drew nearer and I saw Annie being pulled about by some girls. Her waitress's wrapper was torn and her hair had been mussed about. I went up and pulled them away, telling them to leave her alone. They were of Jeannie Aitken's ilk but the most of them – what looked like the entire clan including some didicais from the shough with their ear-rings tripping them and spotted red chokers galore – were down at the far end of the big pen, spilling out into the backyard. And here was m'daddy in his braces and his grey shirt with the brass stud under his Adam's apple and his shirt sleeves rolled up standing toe to toe with some right keelie from the back of the Boglemart.

– Don't you touch a hair on her head! If anybody touches a hair of her head I'll ... I'll ...

– Aye, what will you do?

– I won't be responsible for what I'll do ... I won't be responsible for my actions this day. You leave her alone.

– Aye, you should have told that to your dirty son. To leave our Jeannie alone.

110

– Aye, that's right.

– That's right, Spider.

– He was up the close.

– He can't deny it.

The supporting chorus around Spider began to chime in. Annie and I moved nearer to the oldfella so that we could stand together.

– When's your dirty son going to fughinwell pay for his wean?

– Watch your dirty mouth. There are ladies present.

– Don't you tell me I've got a dirty mouth. Look who's calling us dirty. What about your son, the Hooker-Down? If he's not dirty, I'm the cook off the tanker.

– Aye, that's right.

– That's right.

– G'on Spider.

– The dirty shite.

Dan stood his ground.

– My wee gerl's not used to that kind of talk. I don't want any of that kind of talk at all in front of me or mine.

– You're affeared to answer my question. When is your son going to do the right thing by our Jeannie? She hasn't got a father to fight for her.

Close up, I saw that the oldfella's hand was shaking like a leaf.

– He hasn't said it was his yet.

Dan wasn't going to let on to any of them that John had owned up to the priest that he had taken Jeannie Aitken up the close. Anyway, did that make him the father? As far as I could see it was a lucky dip. For all he knew the father *was* the cook off the tanker. The crowd around us began to jiggle more and more. The girls kept tearing at Annie's apron and some were pulling her hair. I tried to keep them off as best as I could but we were outnumbered umpteen to one.

– It's his all right. It's his splitting image. It's as like him as two peas. Where is it? Where's Jeannie?

– Here's Jeannie.

– Here she is.

– G'on, Jeannie, show him the wean.

The crowd sort of parted making an alleyway and there was Jeannie coming down towards us, her teeth bared in a terrible grin, making a big entrance as if she was Teenie from Troon. She lifted the poor wean and stuck it in front of the oldfella's face.

– There's your granpa. Look at your granpa.

It was a boy and to tell the truth he looked like a wee John wrapped up in a shawl. It was his double – shrunk. M'father drew back but I saw him giving the wean a right double-take.

– Can you deny that's your John's wean?

Jeannie with that daft grin on her face. Bravely, the old man replied

– Aye, and it's like umpteen others as well. All that has got to be proved. Proof—

At that, Spider drew off and thumped Dan on the chin. He staggered back. Spider shouted

– Aye, and we'll take ye to coort, don't ye fughin worry!

Then they were raining punches on the old man from all sides and he was defending himself as best he could while I was trying to keep them off Annie. Again Spider bellowed

– D'ye hear him? He called my wee cousin a whoor. Nobody's going to call that wee lassie a whoor!

His blood was up and he was laying into the old man like a fairground pug. We all backed off down McNamee's backyard, towards the wall that separated it from ours but they were coming at us from all sides, giving no quarter. The oldfella was throwing out punches right left and centre like John L. Sullivan. Suddenly, there was a figure on top of the wall then jumping to the ground. It was John with his sleeves rolled up.

– There he is! There's the quarefella!

– There's the playboy!

– The fughin Hooker-Down!

I could see the look of gratitude in m'father's eyes as John took some of the fight away from him. John whispered to me sideways,

– Get Annie over the wall and up the stairs.

Then, letting out a roar, he threw himself into the thick of it

112

like Targa the Terrible. This took up the attention of most of them and I was able to shin over the wall with Annie. M'mother was standing on the landing of the stone stairs exchanging views with Jeannie Aitken's mother in the other backyard. I looked down and saw John and the old man standing fighting back to back like John L. and Gentleman Jim. Annie and I were safe at least, in our own territory. Nobody ever broke territory rights in the street. It was a law that was never broken. M'mother shouted

– Away o' that, ye oul' targe!

– Listen to her. Ye'd think butter wouldn't melt in her mouth and her son a whoormaster.

– Away ye oul' trollop, if ye'd kept your dirty daughter off the streets, she wouldn't be the way she is now.

– Ach, ye never had two halfpennies to rub together till ye came to this country.

– Is that so?

– Yir son's that daft he can't give you the right change on Jimmy Stewart's motor. He never seen a shilling before.

– Imagine! If you had any more wit you'd be a half-wit.

– If you were as witty as you were shitty so would you.

– Away and clean up your back door.

– Oh, I always kept my back door clean, so I did. Not like you. You can't get up your stairs for shite.

– You couldn't get near your door on Saturday nights for drunk sailors.

– Is that so?

– Away back to your fancy man.

– I didn't come over on the Irish boat, I've always stayed here.

– Ah, you're as rough as puddy-oaten! Standing there, ye brazen bitch, while your dirty clan are trying to half-kill my man.

It looked as if they were going to succeed as well. M'father staggered against the wall. I was praying he would keep on his feet or else they would kick him if he went down – although they were not kicking people, fair's fair.

– Is that not desperate. A man can't get a shave in peace in this street.

Lo and behold. The immortal Wullie had come out on the landing with the shaving soap all over his chin. I said to him, hopefully,

– How're ye Wullie.

– Hullo, son.

He looked over the wall.

– There's too many on your father, boy. He's no chance.

– They'll not beat him.

– But he's putting up a good fight. Yon brother of yours has got a good action.

– He's great. I had to get Annie away or I'd be in it as well. But it's not fair odds, Wullie.

– You're right, son. Aye, you're right, Patrick. They need one more Irishman over there.

And having said that, he trotted down the stairs loosely, vaulted over the wall and lined up beside the oldfella and John.

Then it came to pass that Jeannie Aitken's cousins began to fly about the yard in all directions, some meeting each other coming back as the magnificent Wullie went into action, hooking, uppercutting, throwing, wrestling, elbowing, ca'ing the pins from them. This gave new strength to John and the old man to fight harder than ever. At a word from Wullie when they were at the peak, they backed right up to the wall and m'father slipped over to safety. Now John and Wullie held them off. Most of the blows were being aimed at John but Wullie was cutting them off. After another big effort came a quick word from Wullie and John slipped over the wall as well. That left Wullie fighting the lot on his own. What a man.

But Wullie was using his brains as well as his fists for as soon as all the crowd realised that the oldfella and John had got to the safety of their own territory, the scrapping began to peter out around Wullie. What were they fighting him for? The enemy had escaped. It stopped.

– We're not fighting you, Wullie.

– Nobody here's at varriance with you, Wullie.

– On my side, I'm not at varriance with anybody here for that matter.

– Right.

– There were too many on that man. Ye'd have the polis down here quicker than that.

– Right.

They turned and walked away, talking among themselves, some throwing threats over their shoulders at us and making tribal signs of vengeance. Wullie shinned over the wall and came back up the stairs. He still had most of the shaving soap on his face.

– God will be good to you, Wullie.

– Ah, that's nothing, Missus O'Connor.

M'father and John shook hands with him with no wind left to speak. He chucked me on the side of the chin then, saying

– I might be able to finish that shave now.

I threw a punch at him and he went back inside.

Safe back in the attic, I had to wet the tea because Maggie was busy attending to the cuts and bruises and black eyes. Annie was okay and she had to do John's face as m'mother wouldn't touch him but concentrated on Dan.

– D'ye see that now, d'y'see that? Ye might have been kilt. There y'are now, that's what he's landed us into. We're to be persecuted off the face of God's earth. That's the playboy. Aye and ... Look at ye ... Look at the blood ... Holy God ... At your age too ... That's the fine son you've got. If I had known. If only I had known. God and his Holy Mother would not have made me have him. Oh, if I'd only known. Aye, I'm saying it. I'm saying it. I'm the one who has to look after ye all. Ye's don't know. And try and keep a bit of a home together. The few scraps of bits of oul' second-hand furniture that nobody else wanted from Jerusalem. And the dresser that Maggie let me have. Your Aunt Maggie that's now in Dublin now. Aye, a wise wumman. She's wiser than what I am. And I wonder what your sister Aunt Annie in Derry would say if she could see you all now, eh? Ah-dear-dear-a-dear. I know what she would say. She would say ye's are a disgrace. Aye, I wish I was in Dublin. I wish I was away ou' a this. Away from the lot of ye. An' get my head shired of the lot of ye. Ye's have my heart broke! Look at ye. The blood. Look at your face. A man

115

past middle age. Is there to be no peace for us at all in this world?

The first tear from my mother's eyes mingled with the blood on the oldfella's face.

22

May I
Be the only one to say I
Really fell in love the day I
First set eyes on you ...

Tammy Munn with his wireless on and he and I sitting listening to it in the den. *The Variety Parade.* Rudy Vallee.

Stand and drink a toast once again,
Let every loyal Maine man sing!
Then drink to all the happy hours,
Drink to the careless days,
Drink to Maine our Alma Mater,
The college of our hearts always!

College boys with their plus-fours, criss-cross stockings, bow ties, racoon coats, hats turned up in front and specs. Holding a megaphone. You saw them in the pictures. Rah-rah-rah! Jack Oakie. Slide, Kelly, Slide! Drum-Majorettes wiggling their bums. Yanks. Of Thee I Sing. The Stein Song. The Star-Spangled Banner.

Some day away to America signing on a tramp in the harbour a Baron boat or one of Holts when you can get the chance maybe a last-minute jump and away straight out past Arran straight across the stretch of sea endless with the New York skyscrapers at the other side.

Kate Smith. When the Moon Comes Over the Mountains. George Formby. A great big blackbird with its claws came and tore off my girl's – jumper. Phil Regan the sweet Irish tenor. So before we start romancing darling let me put you wise to that little devil dancing in your laughing Irish eyes. Stanley Holloway. Sam, Sam, pick up tha musket, Sam. But Sam said – noa. Sanders of the River. Leslie Sands. Bosambo. Paul Robeson. Aye-Ee-O-Ko! Sandi the strong Sandi the wise, righter of wrong, hater of lies. Oh, ma babby, ma curly headed babby, does you want the moon to play with? Jack Teagarden. If I ever found that I was just a run-around and I didn't mean a thing to you I just couldn't take it baby lovin' you the way I do.

Tough Bronx accent hi-ya baby makes you think of gangster pictures sez you sez me yeh? yeh Roger the terrible Thuoy Dutch Schultz dying with fourteen bullets in him saying who shot me nobody shot me Edward G. Robinson natty double-breasted black overcoats fitting close round the waist very gallus carrying their violin cases as they go to music practice or a golf bag with a cannon inside snap fedora down over the eyes hi-ya babe the king of them all Al Caponey I wouldn't do that to a yellow dog.

What d'ya want to be a gangster and carry a gun kind of flash or maybe the other kind a gentleman by day and a cat burglar at night climbing up the outsides of penthouses clinging to the wall like a fly making daredevil leaps from a balcony to a ledge three inches wide taking desperate chances and carrying off sensational robberies that would be in all the papers the Cat strikes again three million dollars worth of jewellery stolen in daring burglary. Yeh you could do this between ships if you ever went to sea I suppose. What about your service in the Foreign Legion? And don't forget you've got to break into pictures and become a film star like—

Tammy dunts me in the ribs and says

– D'ye'hear what I'm saying to you? You look as if you've gone into a trance.

– Aye, I heard you.

– What was I saying?

Duking quickly out of the way I say

– It couldn't've been worth much for I don't remember.

Tam makes a swipe but only in fun. He says

– I've got that new record of Bunny Berrigan.
– What new record?
– Bunny Berrigan. I Can't Get Started With You.
– I haven't heard it.
– It's sticking out. It's sticking out a mile. *Da-ra-da-da, da-ra-ta-da-da, da-ra-ra-ra, ra-ro-ro-ro-ree*. But I'm broken hearted cos I can't get started with you. Great. A great trumpet break in it.
– I must listen for it. So long, Tam, I'll see you later.
– Come in early some time and I'll play it for you.
– Aye, right. So long.
– So long, Paddy.

Out and head along Princes Street for the shore. John has got the chance of earning a few shillings by taking out some dogs for a walk for a couple of hours in the afternoon whenever he can. They belong to a woman big bug who lives in one of the houses along the Saltcoats shore front. Maybe I will find him along the shore.

Through the railway-crossing gates which are open, after looking into the station as you go past. You never pass the station without looking in. You couldn't stop your head swivelling round if you tried. Not a very big entrance just two doors and it is only a flash as you go by but that flash is like looking through a keyhole into a passage away from the wee world into a world which is waiting beyond. A man with specs an eye-shade and hands holding up his shirt-sleeves peers from the ticket office. A wee square of paste-board would take you away wherever you wanted to go and through another door just beyond, the book-stall where you would get stuck and lost to the world and not know time go by as you gazed at the books behind the glass the colours red-backed yellow backed Left Book Club and all colours lovely girls with bobbed hair men standing with bicycles wooing them dark men guns pointing at you Sexton Blake Kai Lung's Golden Hours or Ruby M. Ayres' A Shop-Girl's Romance a man on a motor-bike coming straight for you over a hill the Red Rider of the Rhondda Frank Swinnerton I Am Jonathan Scrivener Claude

Houghton the Dixon Hawke Library a crook with a mask scowling over his shoulder as a polisman blows his whistle behind him the Adventures of Charlie Peace The Dragon Awakes Blue Angels and Whales with thirty wood engravings by Robert Gibbings Francis Brett Young Edith Wharton Ethel Mannin A Handful of Dust by Evelyn Waugh it must be great to be an author. Then the platform behind that maybe a train standing there. Going – where to? The rails stretching away into the distance going wherever you would want them to. I wonder if I could get into a wagon sometime down in the shunting yard and see where it would take me to. Then the smell coming through the doors. Not stinking smells that you are used to but a kind of tangy smell sometimes maybe laced with cigar smoke from a big bug arriving First Class that makes your heart beat faster I don't know why.

Past the Transport garage, an old Tilling-Stevens standing at the stop while the driver crouches down at the front trying to wind up the engine with the starting handle, you need to be careful they have a kick-back that would break your wrist. Then, at the beginning of the esplanade, the green painted cast iron Men's Urinal where the drunk men go on Saturday nights and you have to hold your nose as you pass by. Over to the palings and look away across the shore. The tide full out.

You can shade your eyes and sweep the whole horizon as if you were a captain on the bridge of a ship. Figures on the shore. Some wee boys playing at a puddle among the rocks. An old man with a deep-sea bunnet resting on a stick and staring away out to sea. Maybe he sees that funnel on the horizon and he is thinking back. Or maybe he is watching that yacht and remembering his days of sail. Only a few people walking on the esplanade spaced out all the way round the bay – halfway the bridge over the Galloway Burn – to the Beach Pavilion. The usual man throwing a ball and a dog chasing it. Holding hands, a couple walking this way along the line of sea wrack which is the mark of high tide. A football match on the sand forenenst the putting green, you can hear the shouts. Out near the water's edge a good way into the distance a lone figure jointing like a dancer. Dogs jumping about. It could be him.

119

Strain your eyes to see. Yes, it could be him.

Keeping the figures in view, down the steps, clamber across the rocks and start on the long stretch across the wet strand. The figures dancing and leaping like a group on that old vase of m'mother's. He would be skylarking with the dogs.

The group moving farther away. Begin trotting. Now they've stopped again. He's throwing stones into the sea the dogs chasing after them.

–John, o-oh! John, o-oh!

He takes no notice.

–John, o-oh! John, o-oh!

No. Cup your hands around your mouth.

–Camerad – o-o!

He stops throwing stones, turns in this direction. I hear a voice from over the sand answering with the song.

I know it's him. Run the rest of the way. He walks towards me the dogs at his side. He has them in great control.

–Hello, Patrick.

–Jak-Wes the Ape escapes again!

–Ha-ha-ha!

–I thought you might be along here. I was going for a walk. They're great dogs you've got. What's that one there? I've never seen one of them before.

–It's a Saluki.

–A Saluki? That's the first time I've heard of that. It's a great looking dog.

–And this is a Borzoi.

–And they're two Alsatians, aren't they?

–Aye. Rinty and Kim. Watch this. Here Rinty! Here Rinty!

He throws a stick out into the waves and Rinty takes off fast, plunges into the sea and comes back with the stick in his mouth. Then he puts them all on the lead again and we begin to walk along the water's edge.

–How's your face, John.

You can still see the cuts and bruises.

–Ach, it's all right. That's nothing. It'll soon be healed up ... But it's not the end of it. Not by a long chalk. There's more to come.

120

He looked straight ahead of him, taking a tighter grip on the dog leads, his jaw grim like Gary Cooper's.

– Is there, John?

– I think there's going to be a showdown, Patrick.

I gulped. He continues in a tense voice,

– ... I hear Puddin' Dodds the fighting man is out looking for me. He says he'll half-kill me when he gets me.

Jeannie Aitken's cousin from Stevenston.

– What'll ye do, John?

– I'm not afraid of him. He'll be Black Puddin' Dodds when I've finished with him.

– That's the stuff to give them.

– If I could get him by himself. If he would fight man to man. But he works in a gang. They get you by yourself and beat you up. I've got to watch out where I'm walking. Stevenston's barred for me the now.

– I wish him and his gang would come along the shore now. The dogs would soon fix them. You wouldn't see them for stoor.

– Aye, that's right, Patrick ... There's to be a coort case as well. I hear they're going to take me to coort.

– They'll try and send you to jail.

– Aye, they'll try. They tried to keep it a secret but I got word. They're going to spring a summons on me suddenly when I'm not expecting it.

– They'll put you in jail, John. Don't let them put you in the jail.

– They'll try. Let them try. I'll find a way to beat them. I'll beat them all yet.

– Good old Jak-Wes.

I believe him. John will win. John will beat them. No matter how many of them. John will outwit them somehow. They'll be lucky if they get him into coort. And if they try to put him in jail it won't hold him. John will find a way to beat them all.

I didn't know then that I was cast for a leading part in the showdown.

23

The next afternoon, Friday, I had a few bob in my pocket still left from the *Lord Dalwhinnie* pay-off and I was on my way to see if I could find Charlie and maybe take a trip out to Bonaldi's billiard saloon and find a pair of cows to take on in a foursome at snooker. I was going past the Lyric when Eesky Dan walked from the corner and shouted me over.

— Hi, Connor!

He always called everyone by their second name to show that he was tough.

— I've got a handle to my jug. What d'ye want?

— All right, Pat. Here, I want to speak to you.

He was looking, as usual, from under lowered lids like Doctor Mabuse or the Silent Menace or somebody and I hoped he wasn't going to land me one because I didn't have time for a fight just at that minute but maybe he was only on the tap and if so his luck was dead out, I wouldn't give him a fright if I was a ghost.

But what he wanted was for me to join him in a poghle. There was a school in Sleek Norwood's wash-house at which there were four visitors from Glasgow with money to lose. The game was Rummy. He was broke but he heard I had a few bob from the red-leading and so I was to put up his ante as well as my own, stand on his right and push cards to him and skin those Glasgow keelies. There was another local in the game and the three of us plus Dan's knuckleduster would be enough to handle any trouble that might come up.

Why not. I went into the school with him, giving him two bob to start him off. It was sixpenny ante Rummy so we had to win quickly within the first few hands. Of course we entered the school separately as if we hadn't been together and chyacked and slanged each other rotten as soon as we met to lead the others up the garden. Just before Dan's deal I got hold of the deck and stacked the cards so that he must get a good hand making sure I was standing on his right. What he had to do then was to let me get a look at his hand without the others copping on so that I could throw out the cards he needed for him to pick up and get Rummy. As simple as that.

He won the third hand, keeping him in the school then began to win steadily, me being careful not to make it too obvious and let somebody else win a hand now and again and win one myself as well. With somebody pushing cards to you and stacking up the deal, the chances of winning are about ten times as good as the other players and the money began to come in like from a busted gas meter until we rooked the visitors right out. The only thing I began to worry about was getting a fair cut from Dan at the end of the game for he was as twisted as tarry rope and had poghled everybody he had ever been in contact with including his mother, the priest and the Little Sisters of Charity.

But he coughed up all right at the end of the game. We had arranged to meet next door in the top room of the Castle Hill Vaults and he paid me back the two shillings then gave me my share of the winnings. Having a few bob anyway, I wasn't too worried about getting an equal whack. Besides, I didn't fancy going to Bonaldi's without teeth as I might fancy a fish supper later on.

We had got out of the school without much trouble. One of the Glasgow blocks had begun to make cracks and look a bit suspicious and moan a bit about the money he'd lost. But Dan let him have a private view of his knuckleduster and he stopped being suspicious on the spot and became very pally all of a sudden.

Up there in the Vaults, Eesky was in as good a mood as it was possible for him to be, that is, he was only glowering instead of his usual scowling – he was always at his best after a good swindle – and began to treat me almost as his own level, snakes level, that is. I was under age for drinking but he said that was nothing to him would I like a glass of wine, you could get it in there for threepence a glass, it was only wine. I said you bet and he went away and came back up the stairs with a tray and two big scooshers of light brown coloured Eldorado. He said this was great stuff, easy to drink. I tried it and so it was, very sweet, you could drink it like lemonade.

– I'd better drink this quick in case the polis take a look in here and lift me.

– That's all right. You've nothing to worry about.

– It's all right for you. You're older than me but I'm under age.

– You can hear anybody coming up the stone stairs a mile away. And d'y'see this wee door in the corner? That takes us down to the back door and we're away.

– You know all about it.

– I should. I've been coming here for years. Since I was younger than you.

– How young was that?

– How young? I used to come here and get my sucking bottle filled. What do you think I was reared on?

– Ha-ha-ha.

– In any case, it's your turn to buy the next drink. Give me the money and I'll get them.

It was quiet up in this room. There was only the two of us there. But you could hear a bit of a buzz coming from the bar downstairs. There was a coal fire burning in a big fireplace. Eesky came back with another tray-load.

– I got a double lot this time to save me going back down.

– Here's tae us.

– Wha's like us?

– Not they keelies from Glasgow anyway. We took their breeks, didn't we?

– Aye, we did that.

The flames dancing in the fireplace glowed more clearly. The blue and green at the heart began to stand out. I knew what it was, happiness was flame coloured at threepence a glass. Why didn't I see that Eesky Dan Huggins was such a great lad before. He was a great lad. He didn't care. He cheeked the teachers. A tough guy all right. But one of the best. They could send him to the Reformatory but they couldn't get him down. Oh no, not Eesky. I shook hands with him and as I shook hands I laughed. When he patted me on the back I laughed even more. I went on laughing. I was laughing a lot. I hadn't laughed so much for a long time.

I was still laughing as we went down the stairs. Of course he could have that two shillings back and another shilling on top of that to make three shillings. It was the most natural thing in the world. It was automatic. Why hadn't he asked me before? And what about another tanner on top to show that my heart was in the right place? He didn't expect that, did he? That was a great laugh as well.

Laughing, I saw wet roads going past a window so I knew we were on a bus. What a joke. A bus. That was a good one. An A.1. bus at that.

We got off at the war memorial opposite Our Lady Star of the Sea, the church where I made my first Communion. I made my first Communion in this church and here I was outside the gate slugging from a bottle which we had got, filled with wine, from the pub. That was a joke if there ever was one. If only Father Reilly could see me now. I told Eesky this and we both doubled up. Then we sang a song all the way down Hamilton Street.

– *Murphy, McCarthy, McGinty and McGee,*
Of Irish pedi-ga-ree
And nation-al-itee.
Shoulder to shoulder
We'll fight against the foe . . . .
More than a touch of ras-cal-itee
But saved by a bit of hil-ar-itee,
Murphy, McCarthy, McGinty and McGee!

Then we were in Bonaldi's billiard saloon and then we were being thrown out of Bonaldi's billiard saloon still singing. A stop to drink some more from the bottle in a shelter on the braes then into another bus and off again into the wee back room of another pub then Tommy McCann's face appeared then Christy Hallan's singing *Where the Blue of the Night Meets the Gold of the Day.* Tommy went to school with me and Christy can sing like Bing Crosby and is in great demand in the pubs. Tommy is very big for his age and he passes for drinking level easily. He had no money and I bought drinks for him so he joined our company. Another pub, lights, singing.

The Cross Keys.
This was Stevenston.

I could drink in the back rooms and passages as long as I kept out of sight. Dan and Tommy got the drinks but I paid for most of them and I was glad to do it at threepence a glass, whoever heard of a better bargain than that what a laugh.

Christy's face and voice had faded away out of the picture but Tommy McCann was great company and began to sing himself in and out of umpteen pubs. We harmonised with him and we had a good old sing-song. Then we passed the *De Luxe* picture house and came to a church hall where there was a dance going on. That was a great idea. A dance. All the lassies. Maybe see something home. Great stuff. What a laugh. We went in.

The band was a saxophone, trumpet, accordion and drums. *The Brig O' Doon Jumpers* painted on the big drum. Even with all the bright lights showing you up as you came in and all eyes turning towards you there was no time to get a red face. I couldn't stop laughing long enough to get a red face anyway as I made my way to the end of the hall where all the fellas were standing together. I didn't take my coat off as there was a bottle of wine in the pocket and it was handy.

I can't dance anyway. I could never be a dancer because I've got this bone that sticks out in my left foot from falling down the Bath Rocks. I don't care much. Sometimes I do. When I watch somebody like Allan Johnston doing the tango, putting in those smart steps, I sometimes wish I could dance like that.

I don't know how they pick it up. They say you can only learn by getting up and making a fool of yourself at the beginning. Then you gradually pick it up. I'd get a red face. And I'd think the whole hall was looking at my left foot – although you have to look pretty close to see anything. Oh well, bugger it, anyway.

The crowd of fellas was pretty thick. All standing looking. Some brave spirits like Allan were up for every dance, modern waltz, tango, fox-trot or two-step and some up now and again but most just stood and gawked while the lassies danced with each other and kidded on they didn't see the fellas. Tommy

and I went out to the lavatory and had a good go at the wine
bottle. Eesky Dan was no longer in the picture, his face had
disappeared.

The wine bottle was empty, Tommy was on the dance floor
and I was codding with some lassies in a passage near the
door. My arms were linked on both sides and there were two
new faces that seemed to be smiling. Two new blokes from
somewhere. Ha-ha.
– There's somebody out here wants to speak to you. He wants
to see you.

They were leading me out a side door. Holding me up on
both sides. They must have thought I needed to be helped, ha-
ha.

It was pitch black out in a kind of yard after the lights of the
hall. You could still hear the music coming from inside. Old
gravestones. A shadowy figure by some palings. I leaned
against them, my arms still being linked. The shadowy figure
came and stood in front of me.
– I know you Connor, ya bastard.
The figure was speaking. My arms were gripped tightly on
both sides by the other two and stretched out so that I was
spreadeagled against the palings. The figure snarled again,
– And my name's Dodds, ya fughin bastard.

The first punch smashed into my left eye, closing it. Then
came punches around the brows till the left one split open.
Next for treatment was the nose followed by the splitting of
the lower lip and the knocking out of several teeth.

There was no body punching and no kicking and no
weapons used. This member of the Dodds clan, the Aitken's ilk
– it wasn't Puddin' but must have been a younger relation of
his – just went ahead steadily working on my face and using it
as a punchbag till his arms got tired. I didn't cry out. They let
me go and disappeared among the gravestones. I lurched back
in the direction of the hall not able to see very well but guided
by the music.

You're as pretty as a picture,
Did anyone ever tell you before.

127

That was me. As pretty as a picture. With my new face. I staggered through a side door and half fell on to a bench. Some of the lassies gathered round me and made clucking sounds. Tommy McCann appeared, took me into a cloakroom and bathed my face at a dirty old sink.

The last buses had long since gone and we were shanghaied there. But we managed to bum a can of tea from an old night-watchman. Then we found a shelter along the shore road and spent the rest of the night smoking Woodbines and trying to keep warm. There was a special train at five o'clock from the local station that took the early morning shift workers up to the explosive factory station. Then it returned and went all the way back home. We could get on to that train without any trouble as Tommy knew the ticket collector and most of the rest of the workers on the station forbye. We would go with it to the factory and stay on till it went home.

Not that long till it was getting near five. Now I was seeing things bare and grey and raw. I didn't feel happy anymore. My cuts were smarting and the bruises throbbed. I was a bit sick as well. We stirred ourselves and began to walk to the station down a bealing snottery street past some miners' cottages which were beginning to light up and from inside of which you could hear the early morning claghering and coughing and spitting.

We got into the train all right and it was warmer there and we were glad to be going home and getting away from that territory. I didn't know how I got there in the first place. I looked in the carriage looking-glass and couldn't recognise myself. Something like Benny Lynch if he had been a loser instead of a winner and had just had his head screwed in a vice then finished off with a cheese grater.

The carriage began to fill up with shift workers male and female. Each one gulped and looked away in a hurry after one sight of my face. The biddies looked frightened to death. There was a long silence which nobody broke until it became un-bearable to me. I looked around them all slowly and found myself blurting out,

– Don't all start speaking at once!

128

It just came out of me like that. Without thinking. Just straight out. I didn't know why I had said that. Or what I was getting at.

The train started up.

24

Two days later. In the house by myself. The last of the dusk. The lamp lit. A very faint singing from the wick if you listened carefully, standing still in the middle of the attic floor, looking across at the chimbleys of Herald Street as it gets darker.

It was a relief to be quiet after all the confloptions. M'mother nearly having a fit when she saw my face, crying, calling on all the saints in heaven and threatening to walk out of the house and go away and leave us all forever. More fighting and chyacking in the street. Annie running for her life every time she came round the corner. Now John had got the summons and he was due in coort in a week's time. He hadn't been seen since early morning and then only by me. He was up and away out from all the trouble before the dawn even, losing himself, I suppose, away up the North Shore or Montfode or the Mill Glen or somewhere but you never know.

My lips still tasted kind of salty and they had purple blotches on them and open splits. They were thick and rubbery like a Zulu in one of those English pictures from Elstree. I felt as if I was wearing a mask. Lon Chaney. In the looking-glass I was like Raw-Head-and-Bloody-Bones.

It was Puddin' Dodds' younger brother who did it. He had spotted me and trailed me to the dance hall with his gang. I would get my revenge some day don't worry. John was in a bad state about it. He said it should have been him. Bitter sorry he was but he said he knew now what he had to do. At this

129

minute there were watchers at every corner of the wee world looking out for him and waiting to jump on him. Maggie and Dan were at the pictures. I wondered what he would do. It was now pitch dark outside.

I had a cowboy book to read and I got into the big chair beside the fire. It was going great and I was at the bit where the good one is behind a boulder holding off the bad ones at the last showdown when I heard what sounded like a rapping on the window pane which made me jump nearly out of my skin. I thought I was imagining things through being punch-drunk with the beating up then it came again. I keeked over the back of the chair. Another fright to see a face looking over the curtain. Then I saw it was John. I rushed over and opened the window. He climbed in. An old rough travelling bag was tied to his shoulders. He untied it and put it on the floor.

– Are they away out?

– Yes. M'mother and the oldfella are at the pictures and Annie's at her work. How did you get up here?

– I came along the edge of the shore from Saltcoats, across the Bath Rocks, over the railway tracks, climbed up to the roof of the Church of the Nazarene from the railway wall, then along the roofs of Harbour Place. Not a sinner spotted me.

– You might have broke your neck. What's in the bag?

– Nothing. But there soon will be. How's your face?

– S'not that bad. I'm taking over from Lon Chaney next week.

– Ha-ha-ha. I'll get them for you someday, Patrick, don't you worry.

He went over to the chest of drawers, opened one and began putting things from it in the bag. He moved about the room, putting other stuff in, collars, studs, his new shoes and things like that.

– Don't say nothing, Patrick. Don't say you saw me.

– Where you going, John, are you running away?

– I'm taking a wee trip. They won't be able to shout in the street at me anymore. Or wait to jump on me. Or try to put me in the jail.

– What'll you do, John, will you go on tramp?

– I might become a hobo and ride the rods.

– You could become a cowboy. Maybe you'll get to the Rocky Mountains.

– I might.

– And see the ranch.

We both laughed at this, sharing the joke about his ranch. Then he said

– I could do with a horse like Silver King, right now.

– Ha-ha-ha. You could see all the film stars in Hollywood. Become a Pony Express rider ... Maybe you will be fighting in a revolution ... You could maybe meet Buffalo Bill Cody and Wyatt Earp. They're still alive you know.

– Aye, I know. I'll maybe see Fu Manchu as well—

– The Sheriff of Dodge City. If you see James Cagney, would you get me his autograph?

– Yes I will.

– And Maureen O'Sullivan?

– Steady up. I won't have time to make my fortune, the way you're going on.

– Adventures. It must be great to get away. You're not kidding me, are you, John? Are you only going to Irvine or Kilmarnock or somewhere?

– No. I'll be going across the Saraha Desert as far as I can go till the sands of the desert grow cold.

– Hey, John?

– What?

– The Foreign Legion. You could join the Foreign Legion.

– Aye. Or Harry Tate's Navy.

– Some people get all the luck. I wish I was going with you John ... Maybe you'll send for me ...

– I might need a deputy. You never know.

– To get on one of those American trains going across the prairie – Oanhh! Oanhh-Oanhh!

– I'd better clear out while the going's good before anybody comes back. I'll have to lie low for a while.

– You could jump a train from the yard while it was shunting.

– No, I'll head into the wild country and lie low for a while. Here, Patrick, would you lower this bag to me out the window?

He fished under the set-in bed, brought out the clothes rope and tied it to the bag.

– I'll climb down first and give you the signal.

– Okay boss. The Cisco Kid.

– Right. I'll be going away.

He was climbing through the window.

– Here, John?

– Aye.

– Did you bairn that lassie?

He stopped with his leg over the window sill.

– How do I know? How do I know it was me? I wasn't the only one that took Jeannie Aitken up the close.

– No, the Pipe Band, the Boy's Brigade and half the Winton Rovers have been there.

– Including the reserves.

– Ha-ha-ha.

– Aye. Right, the signal is Camerado. I'm away, kid. Okay? When you hear me sing Camerado, lower the rope.

– Yeh.

Sitting on the window sill, he put his hand on my shoulder and squeezed it, nearly dislocating it with his strength.

– So long, kid ... Am I not Jak-Wes the Ape?

He beat his chest in fun.

– Aye, so long, Jak-Wes. Hurry up, John, I think I hear somebody coming.

– You don't think I'm running away because I'm scared, do you?

– Och, I know you're not scared, John. Not in a million years. I know you could beat Puddin' Dodds.

– I'm doing it to stop all the trouble. And to stop you getting beat up. And so's Annie can come round the corner without being frightened ... And all the rest of it ...

– I know.

– So long, kid. I'll see you in Tombstone some day.

– Aye. We'll both share the same one.

He laughed. And now he was out completely and I leaned out to watch him making his way along the roof and down by Morgan's wall – the lamp had already been turned down to its lowest behind me. He disappeared from sight. I was getting worried because I thought I heard noises coming from the backyard of somebody beginning to mount the stairs. Then faintly from below came,

– *Camerad – o!*

I lowered the case down over the roof and into the backyard. After a while the rope went slack and I felt a short tug. I pulled it up again quickly, stuffed it under the bed, closed the window and turned the lamp up because I heard feet on the wooden stairs. I stood looking out the window. Then, faintly, for the last time, I heard the song, tailing away into silence.

Then the door opened and m'mother and father walked in. He said

– That was a good picture wasn't it. Lionel Barrymore.

– Yes. I always like Lionel Barrymore. Hullo, Patrick son.

– Hullo.

The old fella said

– Is John not in yet?

– No.

I felt m'mother looking at my back ... but I couldn't turn round yet. Then I heard her saying

– You're taking the quare long look out the window. What do you be seeing out there?

– Jak-Wes the Ape escapes again ...

– What d'ye say?

– Nothing, mammy.

Part 4
A marmalade saloon

25

– Where is it you're going then,
I asked Annie who was getting herself all dolled up like Nancy
Pretty.
– Ask no questions and you'll be told no lies.
– Is it your night off?
– Is it not?
– I bet you're going to the Carl Hansen.
– Listen to him and his Glasgow slang. Can you not say the
dancin'.
– It'll be the Castlecraigs, then.
– Fancy. You must be Sherlock Holmes.
– Sez you. You'd better watch out for they fellas from the
Barrowland.
– I wouldn't look at that gallus crowd.
– Al will be there.
– Al Caponey?
– No. Al Get-ye.
– Listen to him. He thinks he's very smart.
– Sez you.
– Sez me.
– And how.

– Said the monkey to the cow. If you don't go to the dancing, you'll never be able to dance.

– Who said I wanted to?

– Me. I've seen you practising steps in front of the looking-glass.

– Ach, I was not.

– Yes you were. I think you were trying to do the modern waltz.

– Did you see my black bottom?

– Here, you stop that.

– *Oh, the black, black bottom, the black, black bottom.*

I began to wiggle my feet and slap my bum.

– Here, I'll tell m'mother you were doing syncopation,

she fired at me through a cloud of face powder as thick as Murchie's bakehouse while fixing a clasp in her hair.

– Where d'ye get the fancy clasp?

– I bought it with my tips.

She was a waitress in a hotel in Seamill, now. I sneered.

– I'd rather go to the pictures than go to the Carl Hansen, anytime. Here, we saw that Adolf Hitler in the newsreel.

I did a great mime of Hitler and nearly killed myself laughing.

– You'll not be laughing if there's a war,

she said, pulling a straight face.

– Och, there's as much chance of a war with him as there is with Charlie Chaplin.

She began to sing

– *If I had a talking picture of you-oo!*

So I butted in with,

– *I would run it every time I felt blue-oo!*

Then she finished dolling herself up like Teenie from Troon and ran out saying

– I'll have to away, ta-ta!

I shouted after her,

– Al Get-ye!

Her high heels and high giggles clackit away down the stairs.

I kept humming away under my breath a talking picture I

would sit there in the gloom of my lonely little room and applaud each time you whispered I love you. And that made me think of John the great talking picture man, the star of the talkies. A year since he did a bunk. Vanished without trace. Escaped them all in the end. Only his footprints left on the desert sand. The confloption when he didn't come home. Maggie going to the polis. The crying. The hair tearing. The girning. The polis searching all the local towns and coming up with a blank. The Glasgow polis alerted. The Belfast boat men questioned in case he might have stowed away. Letters sent to friends and relations in Belfast itself asking them to watch out for him. The Salvation Army brought in. A letter which I had to write to the *Sunday Mail* – Missing friend's column.

But neither hide nor hair of him found in the whole year.

And not far off Christmas. The first Christmas spent without John it looked like. And Bridget wouldn't be there either since she had found a good clean Catholic fella after all with a steady job as a fireman on one of Kelly's coasters, running between Scotland and Ireland, got married and now lived in Bearsden not far from the chapel where she could thump her craw and wear out her knees to her heart's content while himself would be on a long trip down to Dublin itself maybe.

M'mother came in and began spieling straightaway.
– Princes Street is getting worse instead of better, so it is, with all they young fellas getting so forward. They're getting so forward so they are. Squaverin' about forenenst you with their bunnets pulled down over one eye. And the gerls with all that rouge on their faces. Tt-tt-tt!

I said
– They're awful gallus, are they not?
and winked to myself.
– Bejings, some of them are gangsters, so they are. Talk about the Billy Boys? The oul' Billy Boys. They would walk right through you, so they would.

Dan came in saying his usual,
– Aye, there you are.
– How is Yours Truly tonight?
– Aye, yours truly. Yours truly, Tay Pay O'Connor ... Och,

I'm not that grand, mother. The stomach's not that grand. The stomach's not right, so it isn't. I think I must have taken a scunder at something.

He used to kid me on when I was a wean that T. P. O'Connor or Tay Pay as he was called, the man whose name you say every time you went to the pictures – *This film has been passed by T. P. O'Connor* – was our uncle. For a time I didn't know whether to believe him or not. But you got a thrill every time you went to the pictures.

– ... and a pity you wouldn't get a scunder at the beer.

– A cup of tea is all I'll have and very little else. And a wee bit of that beef ham, I might. Hullo, Sonny Mick. Are you not going to the pictures tonight?

– No, I'm reading a book.

M'mother said

– He's doing the quare lot of reading, these days. Them big books'll turn your head, so they will.

– What are you reading, son – Zane Grey?

– No. Jack London. The Sea Wolf. It's great, daddy.

The oldfella let out a long sigh.

– Someone passing over my grave. Aye, you're reading the books, Patrick. Aye, mind you and I thought you were going to be the great scholar and get us all out of this.

– And all I could do was land in the Unemployed School.

Maggie said

– Sure, he *was* the great scholar. If only we'd had the money to send him on. He could have went right on too. Saint Aloysius and on to Glasgow University itself, maybe. Aye, taken himself up out of this. Away out of this.

Dan spat into the fire, saying

– Ah, jays, you've no chance, have you? You've no chance in this world. Aye, if only Dan had been a better man. If only I'd given ye's a better chance ... Ah, well. There it is. The same old sixpence ... Dan fell again. Every time I got up I was knocked down again like the man in the boxing picture.

M'mother pointed at him.

– And here it was yourself that did it all. You had the chances.

–Aye, that's true. I had the chances.

–The drink. The oul' drink again. You couldn't keep off of the drink ... And here we are. Three dead and another one wandering the world, God help him, and nobody knowing where he is on the face of God's earth.

–Ah, maybe he'll write one of these days, Maggie. Maybe he'll even turn up when you're least expecting it, you never know ... Never you mind. Never mind about that, the now. It's getting Patrick a wee job we should be thinking about. Can that Burro as they call it not get you anything at all, son?

–All they're good for is stopping your money if you look crooked at them. All I can get is carrying bags at the station or the harbour. Or a few shillings hurling round furniture that's been bought at McKellar's sale to the houses of the women that bought it on the railway barrow.

Dan got his pipe out and began to howk at the bowl with his old broken knife. He looked at me over the top, the twinkle a bit further back than usual in his dark eyes.

–Well, maybe something will turn up one of these days. You never know you're luck, so you don't. No, you never know you're luck ... Yis ... When I look back. The chances I had. McCaw, Stevenson and Orr ... It would be a great thing, wouldn't it, Maggie, to be walking down the Falls Road this night, would it not? And going down to the Al'ambra?

–Wouldn't it not? The ould Al'ambra.

–I wonder will those times never come back.

–If only the work was there.

–There was no work for man nor beast, Maggie ... Dear-a-dear. Boys-a-boys, as your Uncle John used to say. Oh boys, oh boys.

Then they settled down beside the fire and the oldfella got his pipe going and they were quiet for a long while, both of them thinking of past days and mostly of John, I suppose.

But John had done what he had to do, I could see that now. For, although we all wanted him back, there was peace in the street where there had been blue murder before. What was the good of sending the whippets out if there was no hare to chase?

And he had made the coorts stick their summons up their jacksie. And given the bailiff frostbite, hanging around waiting for a felon that never arrived, I used to kid him on every time I passed him.

They all turned up on the day of the case, a good house in the gallery, the beaks on their bench, the Aitkens and the Dodds baying for blood. All set for a good show. But when they opened the box, Jack had disappeared. How can you have a show without Punch? The scapegoat foxed them, spanged his nose at them and walked away to far-off fields. What else could you do but give three cheers for Jak-Wes?

Then things had gradually quietened down. The chyacking in the street fizzled out and stopped. Jeannie Aitken took her baby and went away to live with cousins in the North. The Stevenston gang got fed up coming all the way to Harbour Place and looked around for a local mug to slag out for a tanking.

Now, a year after the Hooker-Down slung his hook, it was all quiet in Harbour Place.

God bless our John and a big 'berry to Puddin' Dodds, the Aitkens and all that crew of ceaghy-arsed, blue-nosed lousers.

26

Christmas Eve here.

The lamp shining through the paper decorations making shapes on the walls. Holly and mistletoe gathered from up the Mill Glen around the picture of the Sacred Heart and the enlarged photo of wee Denis that died in convulsions. Everybody dressed in their Sunday best with some time to spare before we set off to Midnight Mass, first m'mother and Annie then the *men* that's me and m'daddy, some men, well, I'm seventeen but still wee for my age.

Sit by the window looking out at the frost on the roofs of the Fenian Row, white in the moonlight. So we can call it a white Christmas even if there is no snow on the ground. But so cold you have to rub a hole in the frosted-up glass to see through. Only the white square of Cosgrove's yard, not a hen stirring, and the white square of the big pen and the white between the railway lines. At the back of that, mystery country, you can just make out the Inches Wall and you think you hear the waves, they sound as if they are whispering under their breath in the chapel.

Think of when you were kids we would be hanging up our stockings at this time, Mary and Annie and me. And whisht away to sleep while the big ones went out to Mass, m'daddy and mammy, John and Bridget. The stockings would hang up on the fireplace, handy for His Nibs when he came down the chimbley, Father Christmas alias Saint Nicholas alias Santa Claus, you never knew what to call him. You would never get much sleep on that night when every fall of soot would sound like himself slipping down the blooming lum. You never saw anything but in the morning the stockings would all be filled. A big orange at the toe of each and lace stockings filled with wee games and whistles and puzzles and maybe some dolly mixtures. Then your present at the bottom of the bed. You always got something even if the rent, the tic man and the Pearl Insurance had to be missed that week. Mary, the wee saint as usual, would have warned us already not to ask for too much or lose our sacred lives for m'mammy didn't have it. Then you all played with your presents for the rest of the day, as happy as hikers, that's if no fights started up but they usually did.

That was before she was supposed to have flown away in her white box, Mary, imagine. Well, you had seen the white box anyway, you couldn't deny that. They had told you it would go through the sky like one of they machines in *Amazing Stories* where to, the moon, to heaven, maybe heaven was on the moon but you knew now that the white box went into a hole in the ground. Elementary, Doctor Watson, said Sherlock Holmes in the Lyric picture house, but notice that they then cover it up and everybody walks away. What happens when the gates of the graveyard are closed for the night? Anything. Heaven on the moon or maybe further away. *Amazing Stories* says a man will fly to the moon one day and that's daft I know for the oldfella tells me a man called G. K. Chesterton says the moon is made of green cheese and he should know for he was arguing with old Arry Sifilus and all that lot of poor unfortunates.

Still and all you never know.

Annie and m'mother leaving. The oldfella with his waterproof coat and his Sunday bunnet. Stoking his pipe, the sparks flying like the exhaust of a motor-bike – one of these days he'll go up in flames – banking up the fire with a shovelful of dross and wet tea-leaves so that it nearly goes out but will be burning up by the time we get back. Straightening up from the hob he says he's got cramps again in the oul' stomach. Then he blows out the lamp and locks the door, putting the key in his pocket because he will be back first to open up and warm the place for the women. Then away along the shore, marching along, trying to keep up with Dan's giant steps, like a sergeant-major in the Connaught Rangers or something, but I think every time he marches along the esplanade he is leading the Guards down the Antrim Road.

In the chapel of Our Lady Star of the Sea, all the decorations, the holly, drops of blood on the crown of thorns, the crib, the same one every year, they must store it in the back somewhere, that grey paper to look like rocks sprinkled with frost from Woolworths. But it works anyway, I always believe I am in Bethlehem although I have to keep dunting myself.

The chapel packed to the doors, men standing at the back, the clatter as we all stand up, the clatter as we all kneel down, the priest on the altar in lovely shining white vestments.

Oremus.

All quiet with heads bowed down I look at the floor waiting for the stumbling footsteps yes and here they come stumbling in out of the cold a slight confloption at the back the footsteps begin to drag down the aisle we all turn our heads and there he is Charles Bickford one of the Three Godfathers carrying the child in his arms wrapped up well against the weather but he himself his face blistered and dirty his shirt torn his cartridge belt nearly empty and the gun swinging loosely in his gunbelt with a great effort he reaches the altar rails and lays the child which he found in the desert down and Ramon Novarro has only got time to bless him before he falls down dead in front of the altar.

His head bowed his hands clasped in front of him Father Spencer Tracy makes his way to the pulpit. John Barrymore is sitting in the second row his wooden leg stuck out in front of him his big sailor's buckle glinting in the lights and his deep-sea bunnet held by his wife at his side. The priest glares around the congregation and suddenly points his hand in the air.

Tha-a-aar she blows!

Ahab Barrymore tries to get to his feet his eyes wild but his wife holds him back just as the collection plate comes round.

A star over Bethlehem.

A star and a white box moving away up over Goatfell the big ocean beyond the priest back on the altar bows his head silver hairs shining H. B. Warner the altar boy rings the wee bell and the chimes echo out from the adobe tower over the village of San Antonio and Wallace Beery looks up his eyes glinting from under his Mexican sombrero strokes his moustachio pats his pearl-handled guns and gets ready to start the revolution the priest was on his side and the bell was the secret signal.

The plate shoved in front of me giving me a fright for a minute I look this way and that thinking of escaping but a big man stands at the end of the row waiting looking at me Victor McLaglen his face dark and nobbly and glistening with sweat he had just informed on Frankie McPhillips are ye lookin' at me you were lookin' at me he says ah sure I'm not lookin' at you at all I say and quickly put the silver threepenny bit that m'mother has given me specially for the Mass on the plate and it is whipped away from under my nose.

The bell rings again and from three rows down in front of me with all the rest of the heads bowed down James Cagney turns and winks at me there is going to be a break-out a message was smuggled to him on the collection plate and

Chesty O'Connor that's me is okay and he's in pal.

Then a hundred men and a hundred girls we all stand up and sing
— *Adeste Fideles,*
Laeti triumphantes,
Venite, venite,
In Bethlehem.

Then crowding out me losing myself in the centre to get past the armed guards and the searchlights my eyes darting everywhere searching for Cagney.

Knots of people outside talking after the Mass wasn't that a lovely sermon grand so it was – I think I hear somebody saying it's always a good one when Spencer Tracy is in it – but not standing very long, just long enough to wish each other a merry Christmas then away home to something warm I run it home along the shore with Joe Townsley who sometimes serves on the altar and is trying to get on the Burns and Laird shipping line.

The rest are in when I get back, they came in the special bus. We all get round the table and m'father pours us out a glass of fruit wine or ginger wine, you can have your choice and wishes us all a holy and happy Christmas then we all get straight into bed and sleep late.

Our Christmas dinner, a steak pie from Murchies which you have to order a week in advance and collect at a certain time, the best meal of the year for us. I get the job of going for it and when the time comes, away with a clean tea-cloth to cover it. Holding the hot delf basin in my hands, the steam coming through the cloth and the smell making my mouth water, I make my way along the frosty deserted street gingerly, if I fall over with it I needn't come home. I make it and I'm safe for another year, the oldfella is standing at the close-mouth to carry it up the stairs.

Steak pie and potatoes and brussels sprouts all smallicked up but a wee bit left to take over to the old lady at the corner who lives by herself and is half-blind and when the dish is empty and returned we will get our deposit back. Then Christmas pudding and fruit and sweeties and all the rest of it, a feed that we won't see the likes of for another year.

That evening after our tea, another good feed, we pull Christmas crackers and sit around the fire and eat nuts and fruit. The gramophone comes out for a while and we play the records.

Beside an open fireplace
I sit and dream of you
In every place I see a face
That time and space cannot efface.

And m'mother rocks herself to and fro on the chair and looks into the fire and, her eyes a bit watery, says

– Ah, dear-a-dear. Aye, and that's ... And I'm thinking where are all the faces. Where are they all this night. It's a sore heart you would have thinking of them all, so you would. Yis, and I remember, and do you know, my mother, God rest her, used to love to sit and look at the pictures in the fire, she would see all sorts of pictures in the fire, so she would. That's your Granny Davison in Belfast, a fine wee wumman, there wasn't a better one in the whole of Crumlin Street, so there wasn't. I hope she's in heaven. Yis, dear-a-dear. The faces in the fire, right enough. Wee Denis, God rest him. Your wee brother that you never saw, Patrick. He was lovely, so he was. The big dark eyes on him. Ah, but sure he would go straight to heaven. Father Ignatius told me, and he said to me don't be worrying my dear wumman for your child has gone straight to heaven. For he has just received the holy sacrament of baptism. Yes, straight to heaven, so he would. What better death would you want than that? And that's not all, no that's not all. Another wee fella. Ah, shush ... a wee fella that was stillborn, the poor wee craythur ... There's something you didn't know now ... Ah, whisht. Aye, all the wee faces ... Aye, and the other rovin' boy, you can't help thinking about him. Struth ... Where in God's name is he this night. Where ... Would you tell me that? In the name of God and his holy mother, God forgive me, would somebody tell me that?

M'mother beginning to get into a state so Dan quickly

pacifies her and shushes her and gives her a glass of fruit wine and makes her laugh then he starts telling us ghost stories. About the time he was a telegram boy in Belfast and had to go away into the country this night and deliver a telegram to a big lonely house with gate-posts and a drive up to it. There were no lights at all, the whole house in darkness and nobody to be seen anywhere. He rang the bell once, shoved the telegram under the door and away back down the drive again as fast as he could. But when he got to the bottom of the drive, inside the gate he spotted a big tree that he hadn't seen on his way in. And here there was a man standing against the trunk stiff as if he was on guard, his eyes staring straight in front of him. But his feet were on the ground and his head among the branches – and the tree was about twenty feet high! Just standing there staring without a sound out of him or a move at all. Dan took to his heels to where he had left his bicycle, jumped on and pedalled away for his life as if all the devils out of hell were after him. And when he looked back once over his shoulder the man hadn't moved an inch.

How would you explain that? What was it at all, an Irish giant maybe that had strayed away from his lair? Or what. He puzzled about it from that day to this.

M'mother told us about the house in Ardinlea Street in Belfast that didn't have the presence of God about it. They had just moved in after they were married and here when they went upstairs to bed at night the first thing they heard was the kitchen table and chairs scraping over the floor. Then, as clear as she didn't know what, they heard the table being moved out from the wall. Says she, Jesus, Mary and Joseph, what's that, Dan. And he, brave and all as he was, went downstairs with an old bayonet he kept under the bed, ready to put the fear of God into anybody that would be there if it wasn't already in himself. But not a thing to be seen downstairs and everything quiet. But when he came back upstairs the delf began to rattle in the kitchen press. She didn't know how they got to sleep at all that night. Then, later on in the week, they got Uncle John who used to be in the Volunteers to come round and while he was going down the stairs didn't a picture fall down off the wall in front of his nose. They didn't stay in the house more than a week.

Then, after a lot of coaxing, Annie tells a wee ghost story that we used to tell the other kids sitting in dark lobbies when we were weans. The story is called *Claw-ma-beard* and everybody knows it. I don't know any ghost stories and couldn't tell any other kind of story to save my life so I have to imitate Eddie Cantor. And then Lionel Barrymore who is the easiest of all to imitate and then James Cagney. They make me do a fiddle as well before I am finished. Fritz Kriesler it is. And m'mother is coaxed to sing *When Other Lips and Other Eyes* and m'father replies with *Murphy Sat on the Top of the Cart.* They make Annie and I sing a round for two voices.

> *Warble for us,*
> *Echo sweet,*
> *Echo sweet,*
> *Softly now our songs repeat.*

And when m'mother begins to get a bit wet-eyed again because that's a song John got at school, the brave Dan gets up and dances the great break-down to the tune of,

> *For the bright boy was Barney*
> *To wed Norah Carney,*
> *The purtiest girl in the town,*
> *Mind that!*

Till Maggie tells him Missus Brannif will be knocking up. And we all sing the great songs and tell the quare old stories and have a lovely time till the fire is getting low and our eyes are tired and we've all had the great day, the great day, m'father says, and before going to bed m'mammy has another wee look in the fire, seeing what she sees.

> *And when the cooling embers die,*
> *Just as your love has too,*
> *There's nothing in that fireplace*
> *But broken dreams of you.*

27

I don't know where I got the nerve from. Only swanky people go in. You'll see plenty of Academy mugs and up-the-street-ones and people who wear a collar and tie on week days and men with plus-fours and women with permanent waves. I've seen wee Mister Toner in there as well talking to the girl behind the counter. She is very stuck up and up-the-street and wouldn't see you in her road. But anyway, one day, after hanging about outside for a long time trying to get my nerve up, I took a deep breath, closed my eyes and joined the public library.

And here I was looking for a book. It was great in there. I usually stayed till they closed. It was the smell of the books, kind of fusty and you never knew what you were going to find when you opened the covers. All the books had brown leather batters with gold letters and wee specks of dirt on the front pages. Some of them were very old and tattered and dirty with what looked like blood smudged over them and sometimes snotters you would think. I'm sure it was ceagh I've even seen on some pages.

There were great big high-class looking books that lay on their sides on one shelf but I never went over there as it was usually crowded with swanky people talking very pan loaf. I saw a girl with a fur coat over there once and she had a wristlet watch on forbye.

Sometimes you could snitch a look at books with dirty bits in them. That is, if you could find a corner by yourself so that you wouldn't get a red face with people looking at you. All that stuff about it being too big oh stop and he lay on top of her and about he touched her naked flesh and she trembled when he touched it and about breasts swelling and his passion mounting. One guy writes a lot of good stories like that and I am steadily getting through them all. I read it every time I go in if it's on the shelf because well dare I take it home, m'mother would have a canary fit. I cannot remember his name but one of the stories is called Up or is it Down In Michigan or Wyoming or somewhere like that in the States and oh boy it's hot stuff all right.

But I couldn't hang about this night as it was Hogmanay and I was to meet Charlie Hands later on. I was only there to get a book for Sunday. So I just took out one book, a cowboy called *The Tonto Kid*.

When I got home the oldfella was doubled up with cramps in the stomach and m'mother was very worried till he got over it which took about fifteen minutes. Then, after I had my tea, she began to worry me and warn me not to stay out late this night or be going to that oul' corner where the men would meet at twelve o'clock outside the town hall to see in the New Year and smash bottles.

– Them and their oul' Ne'erday as they call it. That's not for you, it's only an oul' heathen festival so it is. Them and their Rabbie Burns. A dirty profligate, God forgive me, that I wouldn't give daylight to. Him wearing his tammie shanter, he's roasting in hell, so he is. I'd give him the immoral memory, I'd give him a kick in the backside. The immoral memory right enough. Says he, a man's a man for a' that, ses he. And him sinning his soul all the time. I'm sure his soul is as black as Toal's cloak. Yis, as black as Toal's cloak. No, you stick to your own holy festival of Christmas and let them have their feast and may God give them the good of it and don't be coming in here late and your father not well or I'll turn another pin in your nose, me boy.

Anyway, we had our plans all made. I was seventeen and we were all going to say we were eighteen if anybody asked us, and go into the Castle Hill Vaults and upstairs to the back-room where I had been with Eesky Dan before and get Eldorado wine at threepence a glass. Then later go halfers for a half-bottle of British Sherry to see in the New Year. We weren't worried about it being a pagan feast if that's what it was. We might even go first-footing after midnight. It was our first ne'erday booze.

So we met outside the Vaults in Hill Street and duked down the stone passage and up the back stairs without anybody in the bar seeing us. Charlie, because he is very powerfully built with very broad shoulders and looks older than me, went down for the drinks all the time and brought them up on a tin tray. The wine was sweet and easy to drink, just like lemonade, no bother at all. So we stowed into it.

Later, Christy Hallan came in and stood us a drink and sang *Temptation* like Bing Crosby, you couldn't tell the difference. To tell the truth, sometimes Christy sounds better, no swanking.

The bars were being allowed to stay open half-an-hour later till half-past-nine that night it being Hogmanay, imagine. And here it was chucking-out time before you could say slangevar, the stone passage downstairs packed with drunk men all singing and every one with a bottle in his pocket. Well, we were all right, we had our half-bottle of British sherry.

Outside the cold but you don't feel it Hill Place is a lovely wee street why did you not realise this before along to P. Marrons the sookers in the window gi'es a sooker when a wean the lamps shine on the streets some with their mantles popping you are by yourself now where's Charlie that girl and her mother you see them up and down Glasgow Street now and again but passing now you stop them and tell her mother that the daughter is the most beautiful girl in the town you have never spoken to them before in your life but you have the nerve for anything you are a hero you stop two polismen and tell them that this is the finest wee town in the world it's great it's a lovely wee town so it is isn't it a great wee town this and the polis are pretty good fellas as well they're not bad at all you've seen worse so you have the two polismen standing laughing the capes wet it must be raining but you can't feel anything why are you lying on the ground but you're up again the town clock face shining men's faces all laughing crowds singing horns blowing the shipyard horn the harbour whistle the Shell-Mex all the boats in the harbour blowing all the trains pheeping the crash of bottles smashing why are you seeing all the stars in the sky counting all the stars in the sky because you are lying on your back on the pavement but you are up

150

again for auld lang syne m'dear for auld lang syne we'll tak a cup o' kindness yet for the sake of auld lang syne Charlie again his uncle Paddy Symmons a bottle drink on the stairs oilcloth you wake up lying on the landing in the dark you've spewed down between your jacket and your shirt a guid New Year tae ane and a'.

28

Fed up, I sat in the den without a tosser, thinking of my troubles. There was blue murder after the Ne'erday boozing carry-on. M'mother shouting, crying, throwing plates about, threatening to leave the house forever, threatening to put me out on the cold stones. Now, three weeks after, although calmed down a bit, she was still thrawing with me.

Through all this, the oldfella had got worse. He had more pains in the stomach, worse than ever and his eyes had become yellow-tinged and his skin the colour of an Orangeman on the twelfth of July. When the doctor came to see him he said he had the jandies. So now he was in bed all the time and had got very thin.

You couldn't get a bag to carry at the harbour or the station to save your life. Not a tosser to be made anywhere and we were still getting *Ivanhoe* at the Unemployed School. I stuck in the den as much as I could, letting the snooker balls lull me into a trance.

Tommy Munn sat down beside me and said

— Have you heard *Rhapsody in Blue*?

— Aye. And I saw it in the pictures in *The King of Jazz* forbye. That fella in the blue cloak coming up out of the floor playing his clarinet. It's sticking out, isn't it? John Boles singing *The Song of the Dawn*.

— It's sticking out a mile. Paul Whiteman.

151

– They say he invented jazz.

– No, it was the darkies on the Mississippi.

Tam twanged a blue note on his guitar. I said

– Do you like George Gershwin?

– I'm daft about his music.

– So am I. D'ye know *Liza*?

– No. But I've had my hole from The Ghost.

We had a laugh at this then Tam broke into a chorus of *Liza*, jamming it a bit and putting in some nice Eddie Lang touches.

I hummed a bit then asked him if he had heard the Mills Brothers doing *I Got Rhythm*. In answer he played a chorus of it. A bit of a crowd began to gather round him then and they coaxed him to plug in and play electric style and when I left he was picking out *The Pagan Love Song* – *again*.

Dan was sitting up in bed. M'mother brought over a bowl from the hob. I went over to the window.

– Here Dan, try and take a wee sup of this now.

– Aye, I'll take a wee spoonful.

– The doctor says he'll be in again in the morning.

– Yes, he's very good. He's a great wee doctor, so he is. I always had great faith in him.

He couldn't take much of the soup.

– It's the oul' stomach. The oul' stomach's gone.

– That's what the good broth is for. To make you better. Put the strength back into you.

– It's the past life is catching up with me. I know it. The past life ... A bunch of the boys were whooping it up ... In a marmalade saloon ... A marmalade saloon right enough. The past life. I drank stuff that would kill a horse, never mind Dangerous Dan Mulgrew.

Maggie said

– Ah well, you would be darin'. If they hadn't been darin' you, you wouldn't never have done half the things you did.

– Darin'. They were getting me on half the time. I think they were taking the quare fiver out of me half the time.

– There wasn't a dare that you wouldn't take. Well dar' ye

Dan, your mother, God rest her, used to say. Well dar' ye.

– Well dar' ye right enough.

– They got you on to drink that stuff in the factory, wouldn't it burn the stomach out of a horse let alone a man.

– I'm what you call a fallen man, Maggie. Yis, a fallen man as the great tra*deg*ian used to say.

– You're the great tra*deg*ian right enough.

– Are we not going to hear anything from that fella, at all, at all, do you think?

– Never put pen to paper all this time. Not the scrape of a pen.

– You'd think he'd drop us a wee line, wherever he was.

– For the sake of a three-halfpenny stamp. Aye ... An' God knows where he is this night ... God knows.

M'father looked over at me.

– Wanderin' the world ... There's the wee fella. Have you been out looking for work, son?

– I never stop. I've been down the harbour all day to see what I could get.

– Ah, you shouldn't be hanging around that old harbour. Ye weren't cut out for that kind of thing at all.

That must have brought m'mother back a bit towards me for she said

– Miss McKay, the school teacher was saying to me the other day ... Yes, she stopped me in the street ... She said *Missus O'Connor, I thought Patrick would have went on to the college.* Yes, thought Patrick would have went on to the college. Ses I, yes ... If only we'd had the herewithall to send him. She's brave and nice, you know, Miss McKay. She always took a great interest in Patrick.

– So she did,
said the oldfella.

So I said

– Well, we didn't have the money and that's all there is to it. If you haven't got the money you're no use.

And Dan looked at me with his eyes crinkled and said

– Aye, you're right there, son. You're no use if you haven't got the money.

29

— Get away from that window
My love, oh my love.
Get away from that window
I say, I say.
For this blessed night
There's going to be a fight,
There'll be razors flying in the air!
Oh de cost,
Oh de cost, Moses.
Oh de cost,
I'll meet you bye and bye!

The oldfella was saying this song to me. Just saying it like a
poem, he couldn't sing it for he had got worse and hadn't left
his bed for weeks. After he got over the jandies, the pains in
his stomach didn't go away and they didn't know what it was
but he had got even thinner and was supposed to be going
away to the hospital if he got any worse. But at least m'mother
wasn't thrawing with me any more.

Annie was getting ready to go back to her work in the hotel.
She said
— Missus McFarlane stopped me in the street to ask about
you, daddy.
— Is that right?
— They were all asking about you. Missus Cook. Missus
McAteer. And do ye know, Mammy?
— Yes, hen.
— Even Jeannie Aitken's auntie asked me how m'father was
getting on. Jeannie Aitken's auntie. Imagine.
M'father said
— Aye, you see. She's not bad when it comes to the bit. She's
not that bad at all.
— Some of them were saying they fairly missed you in the
street.
— Aye, not bad at all. We're all the waan Suez pigs, as the man

said. Yis, all the one Suez pigs when it comes to the bit.

Maggie said

– You'd better away hen, or you'll be late.

– Yes, I'll away then, ta-ta,

said Annie, putting on her coat.

– Ta-ta, the now. Be sure you and get away for Mass in the morning,

said m'mother, after her. Dan shouted

– Ta-ta, Ginger.

– Ta-ta.

– Ta-ta.

Her feet clattered away down the wooden stairs. Maggie brought a chair over to beside the bed. She said

– Are you feeling a bit better?

– Aye, not so bad. Not so bad. Well, it's a change for me to be in on a Saturday night.

– Yes, it is indeed. Well, it will do you good.

– Aye, do me a lot of good. The Cottar's Saturday night, right enough, as the poet says.

– Father Mooney is coming again to see you tomorrow, didn't he say.

– That's brave and good of him.

– And here, wait till I tell ye. Missus Irving's son, I met her up Glasgow Street, and he was down in London, so he was. And do you know he says he saw someone that was quare and like our John at what's this the place, Hyde Park. What do you think of that?

– Ah well, you hear all they stories, don't you. You're always hearing them stories, you know.

– Ah but here, he says to get our Patrick here to write a letter away to the, what's this, the missing persons at Scotland Yard in London.

– Dandy McLean of Scotland Yard. Yes. The Missing People. God knows where he is this night. Saturday night. Aye, the great Saturday night. The great ones I've known. Ah Maggie, do you think we'll ever see the Falls again. Eh? ... Come on you and I ... And we'll get the tram up to the Cave Hill, eh? Would you come?

– Would I not? Yes ... We'll away to Belleview Gardens. Or maybe away to Stranmillis ... Ah dear, ah dear. Ah stop now. You'll have me filling up, so you will.

– Bejibes, if a man could walk through oul' Belfast without worrying about whether he's on the wrong side of the street or not.

– Will that day ever come? Oh, stop now. You'll give me a sore heart if you go on.

– Yes, a sore heart right enough ... Maggie? When you're out for the paper and your few messages, would you not slip in and get me a wee bottle of McEwans?

– A wee bottle of McEwans ...

– Yis, And that's all oul' Dan will have. Eh? It wouldn't do me a bit of harm. Not a bit of harm.

– Well ... Well, that's right enough I suppose. Ah, well ... It's only a wee dump as you would call it. Will you be all right then if I leave you?

– Oul' Dan will be all right. I'll just content myself till you come back. And Patrick here will attend to me, attend to his Lordship. Is that right, squareshoulders?

I said

– Aye, you couldn't get better service in the Ritz.

Maggie delused for a while, her forehead all creased up, then she said

– Yes. Well. It's little enough for a man. And it Saturday night and all.

She was putting on her coat and, doing this, she came over to me where I was sitting by the window. Putting her hand on my shoulder, she spoke in a low voice.

– You keep your eye on your father, Patrick, for I don't think he's all that long for this world, God help him, and God forgive me for saying it. Then she went back over to the bed again and went on in a loud voice,

– I'll away then. I'll not be more than about twenty minutes. And I'll just slip in the side door of the Eglinton Hotel.

– Right you are, so.

She left and in the quietness after her leaving you could hear her footsteps going down the stone stairs after the wooden

156

ones and even going through the close a wee bit. I was trying to take in what she had told me but it wasn't working.

I looked over to the bed. The oldfella seemed quite composed. Even happy. I couldn't understand it.

As I looked he pulled back the bedclothes. He was dressed in a button-up vest and long drawers. He swivelled himself around till he was sitting on the side of the bed. Shakily, he lowered himself down on to the floor, making his way, I thought, into the coalhouse to have a pee in the black pail. But he steered a course in the opposite direction and, holding on to the backs of chairs, he landed up at the wardrobe. Opening this, he took out his Sunday best suit.

– You wait now, wee fella. Your oul' father's going to give your mother the big surprise when she gets back. You wait till you see this. Oul' blackstud is going to be sitting in front of the fire in his good suit and won't she be pleased, eh? Won't she be pleased at that?

He put on his good suit over his vest and drawers without putting on a shirt then, after tying on a muffler, he worked his feet into a pair of woollen socks and a pair of slippers.

– I'll just sit like this by the fire as nice as ninepence and herself will get the lovely surprise when she comes back with the messages. She'll think it's just like old times, so she will.

– Are you all right, daddy?

– Sure, I'm as right as rain, so I am.

Dan of the Falls. Himself. A hero. Who could beat him? He went on in a very confidential tone,

– Now, listen you here to me, sonny Mick ... I've been doing a lot of studying while I've been lying there today, I've been studying hard ... And what I've come up with is, I would say, a good thing for the six-thirty at Carntyne, a dog by the name of Caesar Light. I've had information about that dog before and I've given the whole thing serious thought today and come to the delusion that there is nothing else I can do but put a tanner each way on it. So I want you to run round to Mick Kelly, you'll catch him in the Caledonian Club playing snooker, and put this wee line on for me.

He got out a stub of pencil from his waistcoat pocket, licked the point, wrote out the line and carefully wrapped up a shilling in it like a wee parcel.

– Away you go then son and the good luck go along with you and if that comes up I'll give you something for yourself, as per usual.

– I'll not be long till I'm back. I'll be like a flash of lightning, so I will.

– Well, don't be striking anybody down dead, that's all I can say.

I hared away around the corner, down Bute Place, through the station gates into Arran Place, past the yard where they sell gravestones and into the Club. Mick Kelly was on the table in a foursome and on his break so I waited beside the marking board and watched for a while for you never interrupt a man on his break. It was a good table that looked as if it had just been re-covered and freshly ironed and it was running fast. There was a good nap on the cloth and you could tell it was well looked after. All the players had private cues and they had their own marker standing by the board wearing a white steward's jacket. When Mick finished his break I got the bet on with him. He took a bit of a rise out of me as usual but only in fun then he said here he didn't want these, they were no use to him and he picked up threepence in coppers that were lying on the side of the table and shoved them into my hand. He was good all right.

I walked back, hurried up the stairs and rushed in, saying

– Guess what, Mick Kelly gave me an odd threepence – to find I was speaking to myself. Says I to me, he must be in the coalhouse having a pee, but he wasn't. He wasn't under the set-in bed among the bines either and I noticed that his good raincoat and cap were not hanging on the door. M'mother came in at my back, saying

– It took me a wee while to get served in—

She looked at the empty bed. She turned, opened the coalhouse door and checked in there. She looked under both beds. Then she saw what I had already seen – the upturned vase on the top of the dresser. She walked over to it, picked it up, rattled it, turned it upside down. But the few shillings she kept in there for the rent and the Pearl were gone. She sank down on the big chair and slowly said

– In the name of the Father and of the Son and of the Holy Ghost, amen. I can't be seeing out of my eyes rightly.

Then she remembered me.

– Where's your father? I thought I asked you to look after him.

I told her he had put on his good suit and said he was going to sit by the fire and give her a surprise when she came back. I told her someone shouted out in the backyard for me, I went down to speak to them and when I got back he was away.

– Run you down to the lavatory and see if he's in there.

He wasn't.

– In the name of God where is he away ... He can't be ... And his coat's gone, too. And his cap. But he's only got his slippers on. Is he out of his mind at all, at all? And the money gone from the wee vase. Would you believe it? Oh, I would believe it all right. I would believe it. He'll be looking for a drink when he's lying in his coffin, God forgive me. That's what he's away after. The drink. Says he, a wee bottle of McEwans and that's all he would have. And I, like a fool, took it in. I took it all in. I think I'm the one that needs her head examined, if you ask me. For believing a word that would come out of his head after all these years. A man nearly at death's door. And here he is, taking the few shillings that we've got to keep us, away out on the skite and him hardly able to stand up let alone take a drink. Would anybody credit it?

– Mammy, I'll go out and look for him for you. And search till I find him.

– Aye, away you son. Away you in God's name and see if you can find him. I'll stay here in case he comes home or somebody brings him home. He surely can't go very far in his state.

After checking Nicols and Jarvies I went straight to Missus Rae's where he usually could be found but he wasn't in there. I tried the Vaults and the Horse Shoe and the Auld Hoose but he wasn't there. In the Vaults I bought a glass of British wine with the threepence and Barrell Clark stood me a shandy and kept me talking for a while. He wasn't in the Ship Bar or the Eglinton or the Hole In The Wall. I couldn't find him. After a while I began to think that maybe he had just gone to visit a pal and would be back in the house by now. Maybe he had just duked out for a quick one and I had missed him coming back round the Wee World the opposite way to me.

Then I met Eesky Dan and he was loaded because he had just done a job in Glasgow and he stood me a few. Then I said to myself if I don't get away from him they'll have to send somebody out to look for me. The trouble was in every bar I went to there was always somebody that knew me. I got away though, but it was late and I was three sheets in the wind myself but holding it well. The old lady would be too busy with Dan to notice the drink on me.

When I arrived home the attic was empty. The door was standing wide open, the lamp was turned down low, the curtains on the window were blowing in the wind and not a soul to be seen. The Mystery of the Mary Celeste. I stood in the middle of the floor with the terrible sad feeling that I was the only one of the family left and I would never see any of them again. I thought of wee Mary, Toby the cat, John and Bridget. Not here any more. Ten Little Niggers.

But I wasn't left with my thoughts long before I heard the confloption in the close mouth. I ran down to meet Dublin Dan and m'mother trying to link the oldfella home. He was stoatin' paralytic but not helpless. Not what you would call a quiet drunk, he was only talking, shouting and singing away forty to the dozen. A bit lively.

– There now. Get him down on the bed. Take his cap off. There ... Turn the lamp up, Patrick, and close the window in the storm.

Dublin Dan said

– I never knew he was so bad Missus O'Connor or I wouldn't have given him any drink. I didn't know he was so far gone. I couldn't see him very well in that dark bar we were in, and me only ashore off the boat, ye know. He carried it off that well, bejays I thought he was in great form altogether. He was keeping the whole bar going and singing the songs. But now that I see him in the light, it's sorry I am to say that he is only a shadow of the man he used to be.

– If only my son John was here,

said m'mother. The oldfella said

– I'm a maan.

– Aye. Get this muffler off or he'll choke himself. Put the pillows behind him. I'll boil a kettle. He's not too bad.

Dublin Dan said

– If there's nothing more I can do, Mistress O'Connor, I must be getting away back to my ship, I have to turn to and take her out at the break of dawn.

– Aye. Away you go to your boat, son, God bless you for helping us. I don't know how we would have managed without you.

Dublin left and m'father, sitting propped up in the bed, pointed his finger out and said

– Dan will ... You wait and see ... I'm a maan ...

– Yes, I know ... Come on and we'll get your slippers off. Look, his slippers are soaken. Aye, you're a man right enough.

– That right, Maggie. The Sarshfield Guards – turn out! You would see them marching. You never seen no marching like it. No, you never seen no marching like it. Talk about Ony Moe ... Aye ... Ony Moe. Look at oul' Dan, now. Skin the Goat. He's like Skin the Goat, so he is. On Saturday night. Dan's Saturday night. Dan's last fling. A bunch of the boys were whooping it up. In a marmalade saloon. Or the Al'ambra. Down to the Al'ambra. The Al'ambra? It would be more like Glengormley this time. Bodenstown's churchyard. Your grandmother used to say Bodenstown. Bury me in Bodenstown. Yis, and your grandfather, God rest him, died at sea. All that time ago ...

I thought he was going to break down but he swallowed hard and controlled it like a hero. M'mother brought a chair to the bed and sat beside him. She began to wipe his brow with a clean cloth.

– ... And he made the speech from the dock. Raberd Ammit. But we kept them back ... Don't sell the past, boys, he says. Hold the past. Aye, and we held the past. No, we never sold the past, so we didn't. Then down the glen came Sarshfield's men ... Fontenoy ... Aye, the Battle of Fontenoy ... Feoch a bellogh! Feoch a bellogh! they shouted. Clear the road! Keep the men in straight liners. In straight liners. You must keep marching in straight liners ... They were all there. Ony Moe.

He was trying to get up. But Maggie held him down easily. His strength had gone.

– Yes, I know, Dan, I know. I remember. Never mind.

– ... Yis, and your Uncle John. That other time. Are you there, boys? he shouts. Are you there? Yis, up the stairs. Or Dan wouldn't have been here, now. Yis, the Tans at the door. Are you ready boys? he shouted up the stairs ... Your Uncle John ... And the buggers took to their heels ... The Tans. The bloody Black and Tans. And nobody in the house but Uncle John and Dan here. Unarmed at that. Yes, are you ready, boys? Took to their heels. A dirty lot of oul' murphydites ... That's what they were. A lot of oul' murphydites. Ses I, run away and shout *Varna*. Yis, oul' murphydites ... Murphy sat on the top of the cart houldin' the crock on his knee. D'ye know who that was? Lacha McGra' No, that's not the same as Lacha McGra'. *The night of the wedding of Lacha McGra'.* He died. Why did you die? Why did ye die? Ah, Conn, Conn, why did ye die? In the Al'ambra. Conn, the Shraughraun. Down North Queen Street. Royal Avenue on a Saturday night. Or was it the Empire? Great. With the mill gerls. All the mill gerls. Weren't you a wee mill gerl, Maggie? With your shawl round your head. I'd wait for you at the end of the road. I'd hear your clogs rattling ... A clog dance ... Who's this used to do the great clog dance? Who's this was the great clog-walloper in those days? Yis, he'd break into the great clog wallop. For the cost of a few pence ... The cost ... Oh, de cost, Moses. Oh, de cost ... I'll meet you bye and bye ...

He went into a laugh which ended in a racking cough.

– Oh, that's a terrible bronichal cough. I have the terrible bronichal cough, so I have, Maggie ... De cost ... Yes, de cost, Moses ... Oh, de cost, I'll meet you bye and bye ...

Without another word, he dropped right off to sleep with a smile on his face and began to snore deeply straightaway.

M'mother put a finger to her lips and began to undress him. His face was drained deathly white and his cheeks were clapped in so that the bones jutted through.

I went to bed but before going to sleep I prayed with all my might and tried to wish him through the night. He looked, as m'mother has said, at death's door right enough ... But there was that twinkle that he had lighting his eyes still – I couldn't see how that could ever be blown out.

Part 5
Poghling the stars

30

Death's door, nothing. He was lining up at the Burroo again within a month.

The day after his last fling he ate a double-breasted breakfast and started to mend from then on. To put the tin hat on it, his fancy at Carntyne, Caesar Light, came in and he couldn't wait to get out and spend the money. He was hale and fairly hearty and propping up Jarvie's Bar in three weeks and on parade at the Labour Exchange in four. Doctor McCann said he was a miracle. I didn't know about being a miracle but he was miraculous for about three days after he got up. Says he, all he had needed all the time was a good feed o' beer.

I was down the backyard in the lavatory. No locks on the doors of our closets. So you have to keep half your mind on your business and half listening for footsteps so that you can yell out,
– *Somebody in!*
But it was your bad luck if you drew one of the McGraws. They usually had the skitters from eating too much progued fruit and took it at a run. They would kick the door open without slowing down and be on you before the words had got

out of your mouth. And there you would be, standing up for your rights with your trousers down around your ankles, not knowing whether you were coming or going, looking eye to bursting eye with a red raw McGraw as if you were about to do the Highland Shitteesh or something, about the only thing left to say being,

– Do you come here often?

When I got back up the stairs there was only Annie in, dolling herself up as per usual, the smell of scent would knock you down. Then she has to pull her stockings up till I can see her fancy garters and get a keek at her thigh and ask me to see if her seams are straight, pulling her dress up at the back. The result is very hard for me, I have to sit down quickly on the big chair and go la di da di dee. There was a banana on the table that I'd been saving and I picked it up, getting ready to peel it, when she starts taking a rise out of me about not having a sweetheart yet, so, putting the banana down, I told her I had that many I didn't know which one to choose. She stopped bashing herself with the powder puff and, as cheeky as you like, turned to me and said

– I think, I think
  I smell a stink
  Coming from
  Y – O – U.

This was a rhyme we used to say to each other as weans when the reek in the attic would become more unbearable than usual. Then she grabbed my banana from the table and I went after her, chasing her round the house. I caught her over by the window, grabbing her from behind and holding her two arms in front of her. She strained against me and kept her hands tight round the banana, stooping over to keep them away from mine. I was bending over her and I could feel her shape against me. She must have felt me against her but I don't think she was struggling all that much either. We were just kind of locked there. It reminded me of Buncrana when we were weans. I had seen her then and I would always remember it in my mind along with the picture of m'mother pulling down her grey flannel knickers behind the bed. Annie wore a pink camisole. I had spied it when I keeked through the curtains of the set-in bed where I would pretend to be asleep while she got dressed. Away at the back of her eyes there was always the secret of Buncrana and sometimes we would flash the memory message to each other.

I could have stayed like that till I don't know what when suddenly the door opened and the oldfella walked in.

– What are ye doin', squaverin' about with your sister, leave her alone outa that.

Says I,

– Well, she's got my banana.

– Oh, I have not,

says she, opening her hands to show they were empty. Would you believe it, she had shoved the banana down her bosom but I couldn't very well say that to Dan or I'm sure he would have skivvered me even if I was the apple of his eye according to m'mother. I could see he didn't believe a word about the banana bit as he looked at the two of us with worried eyes.

– Why don't you take yourself away to the pictures . . . Like the rest of the fellas would do. Where's your pal tonight? Are you not going to take yourself away to the pictures?

– I haven't got two tossers to rub together. I haven't got a louse,

says I, very red faced but using one of his own sayings to try and get in with him again. He stuck his fingers in his waistcoat pockets, which was always a good sign.

– Wait now till I see if I haven't got a couple of oul' beeries under the bed that you would get a few coppers on.

As usual, he turned up trumps and came out with three screwtops which I took round to Jarvies. That was threepence. Not enough for the pictures. Anyway, it was an English picture, who would want to go and see it. That right scunner, with his up-the-street monocle, George Arliss, who is never out of knee breeches and buckled shoes, he must go to bed in them. There he is, winching wee tarts in their long frocks and him looking as if he could be their father. It would fair make you boke.

Threepence. Not even enough for half-an-hour on the table.

But maybe I could get a bet on, make it into sixpence and then I would be able to go six or two.

I was lucky. When I got to the den a big pin school was just forming and they made me marker. That meant I could poghle the stars.

Five Pin Pool. Four white pins scoring one two three four and the black pin in the middle. Balls and score as in billiards along with the score for the pin you play down with the ball. Knock the black pin down and you are bust no matter what your score is and it's a penny star forbye and you start all over again with no score. The marker chalks a star on the scoreboard under your name and you give him a penny which is added to the pool. The winner collects the pool, whatever it is a head along with a penny each for all the stars he counts on the board. But if you're clever like me and can rub out a couple of stars without being nabbed that's a couple of coppers into your pocket. Of course you have to chance getting your head in your hands.

It was a big school. Shilling a pool, penny a star. Frank Kelly, Bowly McEwan, Winky Templeton, Joe Pepper, Gunner Brown and Poker Reid. Scoring twenty-one up for the pool. Then Joe came in and swanked them into letting him play if he would score twenty-five to their twenty-one, you'd have to be Joe Davis never mind Joe Cunningham.

So what did he do. As soon as he got a hit he ran out the first pool. He collects the money and they all give me their shillings again. The winner always breaks the balls. Joe breaks, scores seven pins from the dee and goes on to make twenty-five again without giving anybody else a hit at the balls. He breaks again while they are donating their money to the next pool and runs it out before the last man has paid up.

That's it. The game's a bogey. They all start hanging up the cues, Joe pockets the money and heads for Ardeer and beer and no stars for yours truly. But Joe is good with his money and gives me ninepence for myself because he has won three pools, saying he was away to Nineveh. That's his name for Stevenston, that den of iniquity, heh-heh. Joe's a right tear when he starts, he would cod the breeks of a heelanman. He's the one who first made the immortal wisecrack – *Many are cauld but few are frozen,* one day during a hard winter when there was no coal to light the fire in the den.

I sat down and watched a game, waiting for Charlie to come in. I hadn't been sitting very long before Chooky Templeton came in and said

– Are you waiting for your China?

– Aye.

– You'll not see him tonight.

– Who says?

– Did you not hear? He got a last minute jump on the iron ore boat.

– Who do you think I am, the cook off the tanker?

– I'm not swanking you. He's away. Where's this, I-Ron, noOran.

– Where's that?

– How should I know?

Somebody said it was where the Foreign Legion and the Arabs and all that crowd came from.

It gave me the hump all right. There was Charlie away to sea and me still sitting here like mump chants. But when I thought about it more I began to get all worked up inside myself. I brought to the top this thought that had been inside me for a long time. A break-out. The escape route. Now was the time to do it – get away to sea. Forget toy boats and get on a real one. You've watched plenty of boats from the shore. Wouldn't it be great to look at the shore from a boat? And watch it fade away into the distance. Yes, and then there's the rags, too. Bagging off for the night. The stories you'd heard. That place called B.A. Havana. Any kind of girl you want. Spanish. Arabian bints. Greek girls. Chinese. Frank McCourt had been to Japan. Anything you like. Cut across the way. Makes it come up to think of it. A short time for a bar of soap. All night for a tin of jam. Ashore every night in port. A ride every night. A different one each time. Watch you don't get a dose. Condes Crystals will see you through. What's here? You can't get it. Up and down Hamilton Street on Sunday nights with your pals till you were blue in the face. Following this crowd of lassies. Then that one. Give us a feel till Friday. All you got was *away and raffle your doughnuts.* Walk home along the shore spieling about the ones that got away, next stop a wank at Oxford.

No chance. Betty Nixon would tease you in her close-mouth all night till you were standing up like the big dock crane and all you would get would be a fumble at the elastic. Wearie Nicolson calls them Prick Tormentors. Right. All the lassies coorying in the close-mouth together and all the fellas slavering at them from a safe distance. Whistling at them. Chyacking after them. Very cocky as long as they were ten yards away. Get near to them and they didn't know what to do with it. Red faced and sweating, their tongues tied in knots. You are as bad. I know. And if you ever got there you might bairn them and be the talk of the wash-house from the top shop to the Boglemart. As if you were Doctor Jekyll and Mister Hyde or somebody, it was a crime. And maybe end up like John, doing a bunk on a wagon out of the shunting yard. And even if you got their clothes up you would need the bucket-cart horse and a steam capstan to get their legs open. What were you supposed to do with it?

I took my shilling over the Bath Rocks to see if I could do any good at pontoon. I side-betted on face cards at the big school for a while and made enough to go into the wee school. There were only about five playing in that and it was a bit automatic. I felt so cocky after thinking about going away to sea that I fancied myself a bit and got into an argument with the son of The Ghost – that is, the son of the biggest whoor from here to the Gallowgate. He looks at me with his fingers in the top pocket of his jacket like Jack La Rue and says did I want him to get his wee brother to me? Before I could say aye, no or yis, Tommy Morgan pulled me away. I was skint so I watched for the polis at the big school, that gets you a penny every clear board. Eesky Dan came up and said he had news for me, he was watching for the polis from now on, he needed the money. I said he was kidding. He said no he wasn't. I said that was too bad. So he didn't argue any more, just hit me with his knuckleduster. That was a ring with a sharp bar on it. It made a very neat gash in my upper lip, going right through and piercing the gum as well. I could see he meant it so I went off to find a puddle of sea water to wash my wounds. Tommy Morgan helped me.

Later he said to me I was lucky my face wasn't in stripes done by the son of The Ghost. Did I not know who his wee brother was?

Says I, who is he, Benny Lynch or somebody?

What did I think he was fingering in his top pocket? *My wee brother* was the slang name given by a Glasgow keelie to his razor.

31

That long empty horizon between the south end of Arran and the Heads of Ayr broken only by Paddy's Milestone somewhere in the middle. Twenty-five to eight. Keep your eye on it a smudge then a train of smoke appearing. The shape of the ship gradually forming. Here she comes. The M.V. *Lairds Isle*. They say she is the fastest cross-channel ship in Britain. Bow like a knife. Two funnels. Oil burner.

Standing on the Cannon Hill watching for her. Be down on Montgomerie Pier when she docks at eight o'clock. See if there are any bags to carry. Then nip on board when you can get up the gangway and ask the Second Steward if there are any jobs going. You never miss her every night when she comes in. The answer always no, they've got a full crew. But you have to keep trying. That's the only way you can get to sea. Keep trying. Go on board all the ships in the harbour and see the Chief Steward. Your first trip is the hardest to get. *Have you been to sea before?* Nobody wants a first-tripper.

You watched the *Lairds Isle* lying up in the old dock all winter. Nobody on board but a watchman. Paint all faded.

Abandoned looking. You saw it beginning to come alive in the late spring getting ready for the season. Fresh paint appearing everywhere. The funnels red and black with a thin blue stripe. New manilla ropes. Then the big day when the Catering Superintendent comes down from Glasgow to sign on his crowd for the season. You go along to try your luck. All the regulars there. Gudge McGurk sails on it every year. He'll sign on a tanker in the winter. One that will pay off before the *Lairds Isle* starts her run. Billy Biggar runs the tea bar on the saloon deck. The same Billy Biggar that gave you a black eye down the Bath Rocks. But that was a long time ago when you were just daft wee craythurs. He makes enough in the season to keep him all winter. Lining up for the dole money in his flash Fifty Robert Taylor suits. The Fifty Bob Tailor. All winter between the den and the bookie like one of Lord Inverclyde's sons.

But no luck. All the regulars signed on again and some new ones paid off the Anchor Line. Harry McKechnie comes off a White Star liner on the New York run and signs on as a cabin steward. But nothing for you. We're not signing any first-trippers. Your luck is dead out. You would even have taken the job as chocolate-boy but that goes to Joe Townsley.

The first trip is the hardest trip to get. Frank McCourt got his first trip as a cabin boy on a Baron boat. Frank McCourt. He dived off the big crane in the Old Dock when he was twelve. One of the best swimmers in the town. Great fella as well. Would never see you skint. If you were standing at the corner when he paid off a ship you would be sure of a good drink. From being a cabin boy he got on deck. Now he is going in for his A.B.'s ticket. Round half the world while still in his teens.

But keep trying. Every night when she docks, ask if they need anybody. Somebody might get sick. Somebody might fall overboard.

Once you get a trip on a coasting vessel and get your paper discharge you will have a chance of going deep-sea. Think of your first deep sea trip. Where will it be. Anywhere. Some of the tankers sailing from here go across the Western. Tampico.

Curacao. Galveston, Texas. Some go the other way to the Persian Gulf. Tramp ships go anywhere. Japan. New York. Shanghai. Up the Saint Lawrence. Port Said. Down to Rio. The *Nascopie* will take you to Hudson Bay and the Frozen North. The Sea Wolf. Jack London. The Call of the Wild.

You sent letters. You wrote to the Anchor Line. The White Star Line. Cunard. Shaw, Savill and Albion. The Isle of Man Steam Packet Company. The Burns and Laird Line. Mac-Braynes Steamers. The Firth of Clyde Steam Packet Company Limited. Hogarths. The Blue Funnel Line. You even wrote to Kelly's Coasters.

None of them sent a telegram asking you to report immediately to the Tail of the Bank with your gear and join their new ship. In spite of what it said in the boys' magazines or *Everybody's Weekly*. *You can go to sea on an ocean liner*. Send for free details enclosing a postal order for two and six.

After your first deep-sea trip you got your seaman's book when you paid off. That made you a real seaman. Then every trip you made after that was entered in the book with the name of the ship and signed by the captain. Yes, when you got a ship. When would that be?

You haunted the harbour. When a new ship appeared you wheedled yourself on board. You asked the mate if he needed a Deck Boy. You hung around the galley helping the cook so that if he liked your face you might get the Galley Boy's job when the ship signed on again. But you usually had about four rivals hanging around along with you, some of them trying to work their way up from Clyde puffers. And your last ship was McLauchlin's motor boat. And your last trip, to the Horse Island.

The *Lairds Isle* taking shape now as she bore down all out on the port for the last lap. Time to get down to the pier. The rocky path past the Drill Hall. Cut across the top of Hill Street through Kernahan's close into Glasgow Street. Then into Montgomerie Street, slide through a gap in the palings and you are in the big dock. Duke under rows and rows of wagons, watching that you don't lose a leg through a sudden shunt and work your way round.

Standing on the windy end of Montgomerie Pier waiting and watching with the railway porters and the harbourmen who will sling a rope on board and haul in the big manilla to tie her up. It is always a good time, a big moment. Her black smoke above the old dock sea wall then herself edging in between the tower at the end and the breakwater. She has a heavy list to starboard because, as usual, all the passengers have lined up at that side of the dock to be early down the gangway. She ties up as nice as ninepence.

I even give up the chance of carrying a few bags to be up that gangway as soon as I can wriggle my way through the crowds pouring down and along to the Second Steward's cabin to stand outside and wait for him to show up. As most of the crew know me I get on board easy.

A long time after the decks have emptied and the crowds have dwindled away and the trains have puffed out packed to the doors, along comes the Second Steward, very busy looking. I wait my chance to duke into his cabin.

– D'you need anybody, sir?

He looks at me very sadly. I can see he is sorry for me and I know what he is going to say.

– We've got a full crew, son, and there's a waiting list forbye.

– D'ye not need anybody in the galley. Or a tea-boy?

– No . . .

– Nobody sick?

– A lot of them are sick of the sea and they can't wait till the end of the season. But they need the job.

– Eh . . . So you don't need anybody, then?

– No. I'm sorry, son. But keep trying. You never know.

– Aye, aye, sir.

I don't know what made me say that. It's no, no, five times a week with one night off and a rest on Sundays. And even then, down in the evening if there is a cruise to Portrush in case somebody has been marooned on an iceberg or something. Miss a night and you could bet your tackety boots that night there would be a mutiny.

Turn and slouch away down the gangway and into the pier

174

station the bustle being all gone making me feel even more dumped. Home by the back way to be by myself. Over the swinging bridge to the shipyard. Past Christie's Yard and Harry England's cottage. Across the railway to the Church of the Nazarene. Over Cosgrove's wall into our backyard and home.

Sit and look at the old calendar on the wall. The words underneath a picture say *Paddy Puzzled*. A picture of an old Irishman sitting playing draughts with a wee boy who is beating him by the looks of it. The old man looks puzzled. If you stare at the picture long enough it becomes real.

– Studying. What are ye studying, sonny Mick. Ye're always studying. Studying.

M'father comes up behind me and puts his hand on my shoulder.

– Come on over here, son, and make yourself generally useless. Yes, make yourself generally useless.

One of his favourite sayings. And he doesn't know it, but he has hit the nail right on the head.

That's just what I was doing. It was a way of life to me.

32

Beside the shore at Seamill I was standing waiting for Annie not far from the hotel where she worked as a waitress. She had a short break and I was going to try and tap her for a couple of bob. That would make the long walk along the shore worthwhile.

I listened to the birds making maps in my head and gazed away out to the Paps of Jura which could be seen in a distant haze, it being a clear day. The mountains of Arran kept greening and bluing in the changing light and every so often the white tip of Goatfell would glint in the sun's rays.

I tried to think myself to the other side of Arran, the open Atlantic where I would be sailing some day when I got a ship. When. The way things were going I would have to commandeer the Old Dock painters' raft. I stood facing the Firth, breathing in the salt air deeply, imagining myself on the bow of a ship plunging through the waves heading for the skyscrapers of New York at the other end of the Herring Pond.

I turned and looked inland. I could see the hotel over the tops of the trees and a lane running down through them. Then I saw the glint of her auburn hair as she came down towards me, a waterproof thrown round her shoulders under which she was wearing her waitress's uniform, the white bibbed apron standing out against the black of her overall. She looked even paler than usual under her ferntickles.

– Hullo, Patrick. Did you arrive?

– Aye. Post Chaise. I came in Mick Kelly's *Matchbox*.

This was the name of the motor that she first took me to school in when I was a wean. The one that went on fire one day and burned to a cinder but lucky there was nobody in it at the time. She giggled at this then goggled up at me in that way she has. We strolled down towards the shore. I wondered how soon I could get round to asking her for a couple of bob.

– Are you making much tips?

That would get the talk round to money, anyway.

– Tips? I like your patter. What about yourself. Are you saving up?

– The only tips I get are at the Isle of Man boat or the *Glen Sannox*. And sometimes Gudge McGurk gives me a tip for the two-thirty.

– Sez you. Your patter's duff. You've always got money for the billiard hall. *I* haven't got much.

– Away. I bet you're making a stack.

– The only stack I'm making is a haystack.

– Tell that to the Marines.

– I'm just a skivvy. That's what they call them. I know. You don't need to tell me.

I remembered I wanted to bum two bob so I said

– Och no, sure you're a high-class waitress, so you are.

– Some hopes. Did you come on the bus?

– No, I walked along the shore. Could you give me the lend of a few shillings?

– You've got a neck. So you can spend it at the tossing schools? Bridget wrote to me and said you were tossing your money down the cesspool.

– She says more then her prayers. I can toss a couple of coppers now and again with the boys, y'know?

– In the name! Here he is, talking about tossing with the boys and him not the size of tuppence.

– Listen to her. You won't be able to see me for muscles, soon. You wait. I'll be bulging everywhere.

– Here! Watch what you're saying. It's time you had a job. Can you not get a job?

– A job? You must be taking a rise out of me. Where's the work? There's queues a mile long at the Burroo, these days.

– I suppose you're still making that drawer knob at the Unemployed School. Or have they run out of sandpaper, yet?

– Here. You're a cheeky wee besom ... No, I'm looking for a ship.

– A ship? What with, a spying-glass? Och, you weren't cut out to be a sailor, Patrick.

– I'll get a ship. You wait.

– The only ship you'll get is hardship.

– Here, your patter's hot today, I must say. Did you pick it up at the Carl Hansen?

– Him and his Carl Hansen for dancin'. Talk about Harry Tate's Navy. It was never in it. You're not tough enough to go to sea. That's only for the roughs of the Fenian Raw.

– They're not any rougher than me. I've worked at the boiler-scaling. And don't forget I've been on the *Lord Dalwhinnie*.

– Aye, when she was in drydock. The Burroo School Navy. And then you put more paint on yourselves than you did on the boat.

– Away.

– M'mother spent more on washing powder than she got from you.

– Here, you're getting too smart, working in these big hotels.

– Sez you. I'm not smart enough for some of them in the

177

hotel. Some of they city fellas. They're after you all the time. And they only want the one thing. They're all dirty devils so they are. They think if you're a skivvy they can do anything with you.

I wanted to keep hopes of the two bob still alive so I said
– Well, you can't blame them for chasing you if you look like a film star.
– In the name! You can tell what *you're* after.
– Any chance of getting it?

This made her giggle fit to bust and made me feel big and I felt my face getting red. All I knew then was that I wanted to get away while I still felt like a big man.
– I'd better away. I've a long walk back. Will you be able to give me that couple of shillings?
– You haven't been here hardly any time. Would you not come up and have a cup of tea with me in the wee café and I'll give you the price of the Clyde Coast bus back home.
– What about the coupla bob?
– Yes. All right. I'll give you that if you come for a cup of tea.
– Sure thing. I'm coming.

So we went up to this wee café and had a cup of tea and some muffins. It was a right stuck-up place where they looked at you as if you were dirt. But we talked about the great times we used to have in Derry and Donegal and had some good laughs and I don't mind saying I was enjoying myself even if I was thinking mainly of the two bob.

Then she waited till the last minute, right till she came to the bus stop with me where she slipped the money into my hand just before I got on, as well as the fare, making me promise faithfully that if I went to sea I would come and see her before I sailed.

I waved to her from the back window of the bus till it was round the corner and she went out of sight. Then I made the conductor stop the bus saying I had forgotten my money, jumped off and ran behind the dunes.

So I walked back home along the shore and skinned the fare as well as the two bob.

178

33

—*This is the Dublin, Athlone and Cork programme. We continue our sponsored requests with a record of John McCormack singing...*

Missus Boyle downstairs had got a wireless set and there was a crowd round her open door listening to it. A Cossor, it could get Athlone, and Micky Boyle, being the great oul' teague, would never listen to anything else except maybe Radio Normandy now and again. It was an open house for all the Irish immigrant families who now clustered round the door, the men with caps at the back of their heads and the women with shawls around them and a tear in their eye as they listened to,

—*...my blue-eyed macushla,*
Awaken for aye!

Everybody clapped at the end as if it was a theatre. I climbed up on the wooden stairs to try and see over the tops of their heads and there it was, sitting on top of a wee press. There was a big square box with knobs on it with numbers all round them like the knobs you see on the safes in the pictures when the crooks break into them. On top of this was a big horn something like a giant's telephone. From the box, wires were plugged into a battery and other wires connected to a kind of square glass dish with screwtops which somebody said was called an accumulator. I always thought an accumulator was something you backed with a bookie on the horses, sometimes called a roll-up. Like a double or treble or if-cash-any-to-come-take-away-the-first-number-you-thought-of-how's-your-father.

The horn now started making noises like two cats on top of the dyke and Eddie Brady who learned electricity in Barlinnie Prison said it was that Moss Pharic again, whoever he is. So I said to him you'll never beat the gramophone and went up to the attic.

I had just got back from The College For Idle Young Masters of Whoors, known among the posh as the Unemployed School, where things were a bit quiet owing to the fact that the numbers had thinned down a bit.

Big Alec Ballantyne had taken his summer holidays early in order to have it off with a female tattie howker from Donaghadee and was last seen being smuggled on board the cattle boat among the heifers. Wearie Nicolson had at last been forced to accept a pressing engagement with the polis and was about to move into a furnished butt and ben in Barlinnie, clothing provided by the authorities. Jimmy Anderson had broken into the big time and was starting as a tic-tac man with McLaughlin's the bookies, all because he was quick with his wits, his mitts and his plates of meat and had never been caught by the polis. The day he became the best header of pennies in the Burroo School, everybody said he was cut out for better things, you too can be a success. And wee Swy-Ess McGee had been caught breaking into Bonaldi's billiard saloon but had made a run for it, chased by the polis, and was now somewhere between Montfode Dairy and Clachnacudden.

Only one good fight that morning – between Spud Murphy and a new fella whose mother and father were poghlers from Mauchline. It was the quickest way to instruct any new scholars who were a bit lacking in common dogfugh. But there were only two hits in it. Murphy hit him and he hit the ground. That left hook was worth seeing. They were still trying to bring him round when I left.

Apart from that, Mister Toner had only come out of his doze once – when his elbow slipped off the desk. And I had spent my time smoothing away at my drawer-knob, playing pocket billiards and dreaming away to sea – Captain Kid-On of the Pull-My-Wire Navy.

There was nobody in so I wound up the gramophone and put on that lovely old Jewish-Scottish love song *The Sweetheart of Sig Mackay* followed by the signature tune of the School.

– *The Legion of the Lost, they call us,*
The Legion of the Lost are we,

sung by Tom Burkski, accompanied by the Cafe De Paris Quintet, Regal-Zonophone, Number ZD 04188253. While he was singing I found a *True Romances* and opened it to see if there would be any knickers or corsets and was met by a man looking right at me and saying *Let me be your father.* Ses I, you'll have to see m'mother about that.

Before I had time to do any kind of lust exercises, I heard familiar feet on the stairs and began to touch my toes instead so that there would be nothing sticking out by the time the door opened. I was sitting looking like Simple Simon waiting to go in to confession when the oldfella and Maggie came in.

– You'd better sit down there in the chair, Dan, and I'll wet the tea.

– Ah, I'll be all right. Hullo, sonny mick.

– Hullo, daddy.

He looked a wee bit like death warmed up again and was clutching his stomach.

– It's the oul' cramps again, the oul' cramps in the stomach, he said, dropping heavily into the big chair.

Maggie said

– Too much could beer on an empty stomach would give any- body cramps, so it would.

– Ah, sure, it's more like the want of it is the trouble. I can't get enough to keep the cramps away ... Are you going to the pictures the night, squareshoulders?

– Is it any good?

– Ah, it's a funny oul' programme altogether, what's this it is now, the big picture's all them people squavering about in crinolynes and waving fans under their noses and the fellas looking like right oul' dolls, what's this they call it, swithering or swuthering something or other it was like that Jane Airy, I couldn't make heads nor tails out of it.

– Is there any comic, daddy?

– No, bejase, there's not even a comic, Laurel and Hardy or something like that that you would get a bit of a geg from but this fillum with this ould eejit talkin' and some gerl playin' a pyana and they're puttin' these dots up on a board and here what is he blatherin' about but, what's this, Sybeelius's great sweet, Tapioca or some bloody thing, God forgive me, and then showin' you pictures of these big swans amongst the trees all the time, it was a right scunder altogether.

– I might see if I can bum a half-price ticket and get into the Pavilion.

Even though nearly doubled up, he managed to rake up the usual beeries and when I left he was getting into bed.

I couldn't get hold of a blue ticket for the Beach Pavilion but I managed to get with two bigfellas, Finn Donnelly and Andy Kean who used to run with John. They got me into the *Casino Cinema* for half-price in the cheap seats because I look young for my age. There was this great comedian called Dave Willis doing a turn on the stage between the pictures. He was singing this song and he got some of the weans to come up on the stage and try to sing it quicker than he could, the one who sang it quickest to get a prize.

– *I'm a pickle packer*
  And I work at packing pickles
  In a pickle factory not so far from here.
  I packle all the pickles
  That are packed in pickle bottles
  And I'm sent to packle pickles far and near.
  So, if you're feeling fickle
  And you feel you want a pickle
  And a pickle that will fill you with delight,
  It's a bottle of my pickles
  From the honeysuckle sicle,
  And that little pickle quickly puts you right!

It was a great laugh hearing the kids getting their tongues tied in knots. A wee boy with the arse out of his trousers and the snotters tripping him won a box of caramels and we all gave him a big cheer for the wee soul looked as if he could do with a good feed.

When I got back home I found that the doctor had been called in to see Dan and had given him something for the pain in his stomach. He was now sleeping like a log.

M'mother said he had what they called a relapse, but if they asked her, he had been relapsed since the day they left Belfast.

34

The harbour was quiet. The only bit of interest coming from a tramp flying the Blue Peter which meant she was leaving that day. All the bustle was around her as she was got ready for sailing. She had a full crew I found out a few days before so nothing doing there. The Belfast boat had already sailed – without me, as usual. I had seen the *Duchess of Hamilton* in and out of the harbour without being invited to join her. I had even tried the *King Orry* of the *Isle of Man Steam Packet Company*. Very reckless. A case of Man for the Manxmen. You would need a sawn-off tail to get a job on one of their boats.

Some ginger ale bottle tops lying around Winton Pier after the Arran Boat went out. I got two of these, worked on them with a big chuckie, laid them on the rails in a quiet part of the shunting yard and pushed a wagon over the top, flattening them. You have to know how to move a ten ton wagon by yourself but you soon pick that up round our way. Get a wagon at the end of a line. If the coupling is hanging down that's okay. If not, you climb up, stand on the chain, stretch out and grip both trucks, pulling together with all your puff and bearing down with all your weight on the chain. This should be enough to pull the end wagon a couple of inches towards the other. That's all you need. Then lay your bottle tops on the line as near to the truck wheel as you can get. You then get between the wagons again, put both shoulders against the end one and both feet planted on the other. If you then try to straighten up, using all your muscles, you'll find that the wagon moves a couple of inches, enough for two bottle tops.

With the flattened tops I waited my chance in the pier station till McTavish, the big Railway Dud, was chasing some kids round the wagons and duked under to the slot machines. I got a bar of Nestlé's milk chocolate with one top and, with the other, a Churchman's No. 1 cigarette all done up in silver paper and a little packet all to itself.

I pinched some tomatoes from boxes piled up on a railway barrow and went away down the old dock, sat on a bollard beside the *Pioneer* – one of MacBraynes – and ate my progued dinner followed by a cigarette of the finest Virginia tobacco as it said on the box.

I made the smoke come out of my nostrils and looked out from the bridge of my ship as she ploughed through the ice, missing bergs by inches and mowing down Eskimos right left and centre. I wanted to stay around the harbour for the tanker which was coming in and paying off that day, so the word was. I could fill in time by carrying bags to the Isle of Man Boat before she sailed at three. I had got a good tip from Gudge McGurk that you should see the Seaman's Union man and let him know that you would put a pound down for your union book if you got a ship and pay two month's subscriptions in advance. And this I had done.

After I had finished my banquet and dreamed at the green waters of the old dock for a while, I took a stroll in the direction of the tramp due for sailing, making my way under the big coal hoist that takes the wagons up, rails and all on a lift, cants them over and empties the coal into the ships' bunkers.

All the bustle of departure was around the tramp – s.s. *Palmira*. Stores on the quay waiting to be hoisted on board, sailors hosing down the decks, the engineers busy getting steam up.

I approached right under the bows to watch. A voice shouted

– Hi, Connor! Hi, Pat!

I looked up. It was George Hall, who was now a rope-runner for the harbour, leaning over the rail and hailing me.

– Who, me?

– Aye. You want to go to sea, do you not? Come up here on deck.

– What ye getting at?

– Don't be daft. Get up here on board, quick.

Without stopping to think or question any more, I made my way up the gangway and on to the ship. George was standing outside the saloon door with the Chief Steward and the Union man. The Chief Steward looked me up and down as if he was buying me on a stall and calculating how many helpings of curried boy I would make for supper. The Union man, a Highlander, began to speak

– Now, here's a ghood lhad who wants to gho to sea. He's a ghood clean lhad and a ghood worker. He was on the Arran bhoat for a while in the summer and he's no stranger to the sea. I know his fhamily well. All his fhamily went to sea, so they did, every one of them. And his ghrandfather was at the Battle of Jhutland and lost a leg in His Majesty's Rhoyal Nhavy.

All this was news to me.

– You couldn't get a bhetter or more honest lhad. And, if he's wee, well he's whiry so he is and he'll whork well for you. A right, whilling lhad . . .

The Chief Steward made a sign and pulled him by the arm into the saloon alleyway where they talked together in whispers.

I had been trying to look all the things the Union man said I was – good, clean, honest, wiry, willing – and now said to George out of the corner of my mouth,

– What's going on?

– The cabin boy didn't turn up from the Shipping Federation in Glasgow and they haven't got time to send up for another one so there's a chance of signing a local fella.

The Chief Steward and the Union man came back out of the alleyway. The Chief looked at me and said

– Do you want to go to sea, son?

– I want nothing more.

– Can you be on board with your gear at seven o'clock, ready to sail at eight?

– Aye, aye, sir!

They laughed at each other then the Chief said

– Come on into the saloon, son, and sign articles.

The Union man said

– I've ghot you a berth as cabin bhoy and you'll sign the articles and be a ghood lhad. You'll need a white jacket, or two would be even better. And you'll ghet an advance note. Ask for four phounds and don't forget the hUnion, I'll have your bhook ready and pay up your dues in advance like a ghood lhad. I always try to lhook after my lhads.

I thanked George and he laughed and said now I'd done it and went away to get on with his work. I went into the saloon a bit shaky and scared inside myself and signed the ship's articles in front of the Captain and the Mate. There was no turning back once I signed the articles and after I had arranged to see the Union man all right and been shown the cabin which I was to share with the galley boy, I made my way home at a run, my heart in my mouth, to tell the news.

35

Up the wooden stairs to the attic, two at a time, my advance note cashed by Beef Donnelly who had given me three pounds ten for it. An advance note is not supposed to be cashed until after the ship sails. So what happens is you get somebody who trades in advance notes to cash it for you for ten bob less. He cashes it with the shipping company after the ship sails, making ten shillings on the deal. But he takes a chance on you missing the ship.

I had squared the Union man, stopped at Tuohy's the ship chandlers to buy a white steward's jacket and a second-hand seaman's bag and now clutched these under my arm as I ran up the stairs.

As I opened the door, the smell of wintergreen met me, bringing black shadows which were trying to remind me of something, what was it, beside the set-in bed on which the oldfella lay stretched out, his jaws a bit clapped-in looking, while m'mother stood in the middle of the floor looking out of the window with a sad faraway dream in her eyes.

But Dan's face broke into a crinkly smile as he saw me, chasing the shadows away.

– Hullo, sonny mick.

– Hullo, daddy.

Maggie's face also lost the faraway look and the lines of sadness became fainter as she said

– What have you got there?

I said

– Wait till I tell ye. Wait till I tell ye this ...

I stopped to let it sink in. Maggie said

– Well, what is it you're going to tell us. We're waiting to hear.

– I've got a job!

M'mother said

– A job. Glory be to God. What are you doing?

– I've signed on a ship. We're sailing the night.

She put her hand up to her mouth,

– Oh, Jesus, Mary and Saint Joseph!

– Cabin boy. I was lucky. I was just on the spot when this fella hadn't turned up from the Federation. George Hall put in a word for me.

– Oh son, you haven't signed on yet? Stay ... Would you not stay here with us? And your father here not well?

Dan raised himself up in the bed and said

– I wouldn't stop him going for that.

– It's too good a chance to miss, mammy. My first trip.

– Where's this it's going?

continued m'father.

– I don't know. It could be anywhere. But we're sailing for Liverpool first for orders.

– What's the name of it and what's your cargo?

– The s.s. *Palmira*. I think it's general cargo.

– Have you signed what they call the articles?

– Aye, and I got my advance note. D'ye see my seaman's bag? I got it in Tuohy's. And there's my white jacket. I'll be wearing a white jacket when I go into the saloon.

M'mother sat down with a long sigh.

– Dear God ... Son ... Do you know what you're doing?

– I'm going to see the world – the only way I can.

– Oh, sonny dear ... Here ... Look ... Come over you here to me.

I went over to her. She took my hand in both of hers. The sadness had come back and she was struggling for words.

– There's something on the side of your face. Something ... Here. Come over here to the light of the window.

She took me by the hand and we went over to the window behind the dresser. She pretended to be wiping something off my face. She began to whisper to me.

– Your father's quare and bad, you know. It's serious. I know it in my bones.

– Ach, mammy, he'll be all right. You can't keep him down. You said that before and he was back up on his feet in no time.

– He's bad. He's bad this time ... Son ... I'm telling you this ...

She was struggling for words again. Then she looked deep into my eyes and whispered slowly and clearly,

– If you go on that boat ... your father won't be here when you come back. May God forgive me.

Yes. May God forgive her for saying a terrible thing like that. Something I wouldn't even give space in my mind to.

– What do you want me to do – stay here on the dole and waste my life away? Up and down to the Burroo School or watching for the polis at the pontoon school?

– I'm sure you would get a wee job.

– A wee job. Some hopes. With queues a mile long for the dole.

– At least you would be beside us and your father on his sick bed.

– Ah, he won't be there long. He'll be up looking for his pint and you wait to you see his face when I bring him home some cigars. Cigars. I've always wanted to do that. And he'll be as right as rain.

– Will you not take the warning. Is it not enough – one wandering the world?

– John ... Aye, but maybe I'll find John somewhere, mammy!

Standing in the *Ship Bar* with Jim Neilson and Eesky Dan, my sea-bag by my side. A full-blown deep-sea sailor I know enough to buy the drinks when I have just signed on. What's left of the advance note had to be got through before sailing time, that's the drill. What's the time now? Getting on. The barman worked with Annie in the Kilwinning Eglinton Arms so he doesn't question my age. Eesky wants to be pals again even though I still have his scar on my lip. Oh well. I don't feel like fighting tonight. Buy him one for old times sake. He went to school with me, didn't he?

Drink to Paddy-across-the-water,
Saint Mary's in our hearts always!

Puddles of drink on the bar every time I look on the top I'm double-banked, two pints in front of me instead of one. Shove up the halfs, you must shove up the whiskies. You're the one that's signed on. Buy drinks. You get waves from all round the bar. Big Man. I hear you've signed on, Pat. Dan Watt. Give him a drink. Wish Charlie was here to drink my advance note with me. Frank McCourt's at sea as well. All the boys. A bunch of the boys. A bunch of the boys were whooping it up. In a marmalade saloon. Here I am. I'm at the bar. My horse is tied up outside. I've arrived. The Cook Aff The Tanker. Away across the ocean blue. Down they come, head two. Away down Ry – o. Where will she dock. All the tarts. All the rags. All the pros. Short time, Johnny. Plenty jig-a-jig. Won't be long now. My trousers already bulging to think of it. All I want. Go for an all night on my first night ashore. Jingle the money in my pocket. The sailor off the ship in the harbour will buy the drinks. Get one for the stranger at the end of the bar.

All the lights on the bottles but my mother's sad face. *What was that wee song John and you used to sing, son?* Yes. But lift the glass and drink deep. *Come draw a drap wi' the best o' it yet, go seek for pleasure where you will but here I never missed it yet.* Where did I hear that? Jim Neilson's face. Eesky Dan's face. A ship blowing from the harbour. That's your ship blowing, Pat. That's the *Palmira.* What's the time? It's after seven. Come on, Pat. You were to be turned to on board at seven. I want to sing a song before I go. Come on, Pat. You'll miss your ship. She's blowing again. Jim Neilson on one arm, Eesky on the other. Linked arms. Held up. Eesky carries my sea-bag. Out the bar. The street looks funny. The light is different. Past the corner. They're all looking. I'm the star of this picture.

All the fellas at the corner stand like statues. Bagwash McBain. The Fighting Scot. Monkey Nuttall. Kee-Kee Tam. Rab Walker. Dublin Dan. Moon McMullin. Gudge McGurk. They're frozen. They don't move. I've got a good send-off.

Past the corner around by the jail. Come on Paddy, you'll have to hurry. We'll see you on board, don't worry. Good fellas. Good mates. Shipmates forever for all that. They keep me from tripping over the railway lines, from falling over the hawsers. Come on Paddy, you'll make it.

Christ, my mother's at the ship. Standing by the gangway. Crying bitter tears. The last appeal. Don't go, Patrick. Oh, son, don't go. They're taking the gangway up. Paddy, come on. Eesky takes my bag on board and dumps it on the deck. She's waiting to sail.

I'm on the deck. The gangway's up. My bag stowed away. Slack away. There's a new angle. Where's the dock? Arran swinging into view. There's the North Shore. Away up there, Annie in her hotel in her apron. Go around the starboard side. She's under weigh.

Figures on the dock. Jim and Eesky holding each other up. Laughing. Your mother's wee stricken figure. She's growing smaller. A wee grey cr'atur'. And smaller. *What was that wee song John and you used to sing, son?*
   — Camerad — o,
   Camerad — o — o — o — o,
fainter and fainter tailing away . . .

Aye, and here's Paddy off to box the compass and poghle the stars!

Jack Higgins
The Savage Day £2.50

Simon Vaughan fought a dirty war in Korea, so the British Army eased him out. Ex-Major turned adventurer, firearms specialist with the best of gun-running connections, and half-Irish as a bonus . . .

Now they offer to get him out of the Greek prison if he'll take on the IRA in Belfast . . .

'First class . . . packed with action, atmosphere and ingenuity' BELFAST TELEGRAPH

'Among the greats of the high adventure storytellers' EVENING NEWS

A Prayer for the Dying £2.50

With a gun in his hand, Fallon was the best. His track record went a long and shady way back. This time the bidding came from Jack Meehan, an underworld baron with a thin varnish of respectability you'd only got to scratch once to watch the worms crawl out. The job was up North, but when Fallon got there he found himself changing sides, which put him in opposition to Meehan, a place where life expectancy was very short indeed.

'Tough, bitter, superbly written' NEW YORK TIMES

All these books are available at your local bookshop or newsagent, or can be ordered direct from the publisher. Indicate the number of copies required and fill in the form below.

Send to: **CS Department, Pan Books Ltd., P.O. Box 40,
             Basingstoke, Hants.   RG21 2YT.**

or phone: 0256 469551 (Ansaphone), quoting title, author
             and Credit Card number.

Please enclose a remittance* to the value of the cover price plus: 60p for the first book plus 30p per copy for each additional book ordered to a maximum charge of £2.40 to cover postage and packing.

*Payment may be made in sterling by UK personal cheque, postal order, sterling draft or international money order, made payable to Pan Books Ltd.

Alternatively by Barclaycard/Access:

Card No. | | | | | | | | | | | | | | | | | | | | |

_____

Signature:

Applicable only in the UK and Republic of Ireland.

While every effort is made to keep prices low, it is sometimes necessary to increase prices at short notice. Pan Books reserve the right to show on covers and charge new retail prices which may differ from those advertised in the text or elsewhere.

NAME AND ADDRESS IN BLOCK LETTERS PLEASE:

....

Name _____

Address _____

_____

_____

_____

                                                          3/87